# 30 DAYS
# TO GRACE

## THE PRACTICE GUIDE
## TO ACHIEVE YOUR ULTIMATE GOALS

## DIANE SIEG

INTENTIONAL PRESS
DENVER, COLORADO

# 30 DAYS TO GRACE
## THE PRACTICE GUIDE
## TO ACHIEVE YOUR ULTIMATE GOALS
©2012 Diane Sieg

ISBN 978-0-9848327-0-5
Library of Congress Control Number: 2011962697

Attention Corporations, Universities, Colleges,
and Professional Organizations:
Quantity discounts are available on bulk purchases of this book for educational, gift purposes, or as premiums for increasing magazine subscriptions or renewals. Special books or book excerpts can also be created to fit specific needs. For information, please contact Intentional Press, 2381 Clermont Street, Denver, CO 80207; (303) 321-1010; diane@dianesieg.com.

# 30 Days to Grace
## THE PRACTICE GUIDE TO
## ACHIEVE YOUR ULTIMATE GOALS

*This book is dedicated to*
*all of my teachers*
*who have helped me open to grace.*

# PRAISE FOR THE
## *30 DAYS TO GRACE* PRACTICE

*"I should love* 30 Days to Grace *for helping me lose ninety pounds, resolve a couple of scary financial situations, and get back on track creatively—all in very short order! And I do. But in spite of those amazing results, what I've truly come to value is how I go deeper on a daily basis. My intentions continue to evolve as I do."*

—Anne Parsons, editor

*"I am struck by the clarity I have gleaned in my personal and professional life with this daily practice. What started out as an intention to de-clutter my house has turned into taking care of other clutter, such as scheduling a certification exam and clearing my schedule to exercise. I feel more calm, clear, and focused—not just while I'm doing it, but for my entire day."*

—Dana Hill, RN

*"My husband has advanced Alzheimer's, and I know my daily practice for the last 660 days has kept me sane and my husband home longer. On those difficult days when I don't feel like getting out of bed, I hear you saying, 'Congratulations for showing up today.' Someone cares. That's when I show up. And celebrate."*

—Jeanne Baird, 24/7 caregiver

*"My experience with* 30 Days to Grace *has been nothing short of extraordinary. Leading me through tough times, this practice helped focus my intention to manifest a financial situation I did not know was possible."*

—Anne Macomber, marketing consultant

*"Thanks to your* 30 Days to Grace *I have chosen to focus on the 95 percent of my home that is beautiful and not stress about the imperfections. I embrace the warmth of our home that is created by people, not things, and enjoy being truly present. In other words, I rearranged 'me,' not my furniture, and I feel more peaceful and joyful."*

—Jan Austin, CPA

*"*30 Days to Grace *has absolutely changed my life. I have taken care of countless health issues, including getting an important biopsy, making a long overdue dentist appointment, and taking the stairs instead of the elevator. It has empowered me to make life long changes not only physically but mentally and spiritually."*

—Patti Woodruff, owner of Colorado
Moves Counseling Center, Inc.

*"I love how the program has bundled the essentials. It is freeing to start my day by opening to grace and to indulge in 'me time' before getting the family up and out the door."*

—Jennifer Brennan, mom

*"My practice this morning already affected my day. The 'back talk' in my head has been replaced by my intention, and the positive, peaceful thoughts are much more productive than my usual banter. I feel calm and ready to work."*

—David Corder, personal trainer

*"I have been practicing yoga since 1990, meditating for years, and even journaling for a long time, and I must say I was pleasantly surprised by how fabulous I feel when I do this practice."*

—Molly Hargarten, artist

*"I needed to make changes in my life when I found* 30 Days to Grace. *A breakup in a long-term relationship, financial troubles and severe back pain all plagued me. Not only did I get relief from my physical and emotional pain, but now I'm a yogi, writer and meditator! I see how far I have come over the last year with a new love in my life, my chosen career and a strong, flexible body."*

—Peggy Wagner, interior designer

*"After finishing my first thirty day practice, I was offered the nursing position I have been working towards. I am now starting a second intention with the same expected outcome and am so grateful to this program."*

—Kathryn Bottinelli, transition coach

*"I initially focused my intention on money flowing easily into my life. Through the practice of* 30 Days to Grace, *I saw that abundance is already surrounding me, reminding me that I have exactly what I need right now. Focusing on financial security, something I have struggled with all of my life appears to have fled from my consciousness! I actually feel pretty darn secure, finally."*

—Joanne Dalton, educator

*"*30 Days to Grace *has changed my life! I'm now learning to love myself and my body just the way I am and see that I have a lot to offer someone else in this life. As I practice the yoga, deep breathing, meditation, and journaling, my whole life purpose has become clear to me. Quite amazing and overwhelming at the same time, but I am sticking with it."*

—Tamara Scott, MSN, CPNP

# INTRODUCTION

Have you ever come home from a conference or retreat all pumped up, reenergized and recommitted to practice something different? You feel so great physically, emotionally, spiritually, and mentally, you are confident you will keep this new practice going. You are on fire, full of focus, motivation, and commitment.

*Yeah, me too.*

And then you have an early appointment. Your child gets sick. The dog runs away. You have houseguests. You work late. It's too cold. It's too hot. You are too tired. You plan to start again tomorrow, which turns into two weeks, when you forget about it completely.

*Yeah, me too.*

There are many gurus and masters of enlightenment I have studied that have much more wisdom and experience than I do when it comes to daily practice. But the thing is, I attempted a daily practice for years and could never be successful for more than a handful of days. Until I created *30 Days to Grace.*

*30 Days to Grace* is a guided daily practice that incorporates deep breathing, yoga poses, meditation, and journaling, all focusing on your ultimate goal, what I call your deepest intention. It is life-transforming because what we focus on expands, and when you focus on what you want for 30 minutes every day, your days are different because you are different. It is a simple practice, accessible to anyone. All you have to do is open to grace and show up for yourself.

Let me show you how.

*Diane*

# CHAPTER 1

# OPEN TO GRACE

*"Grace wakes us up when we are asleep,*
*brings light to where there is darkness,*
*and removes obstacles from our path."*
—Krishna Das

What if you could open to all the desires you could think of, even those you haven't thought of yet, instead of shutting them down because of fear and limitation? What if you could open to something bigger than yourself and be held and supported by this energy? What if you could truly transform yourself and your life as a result of this opening?

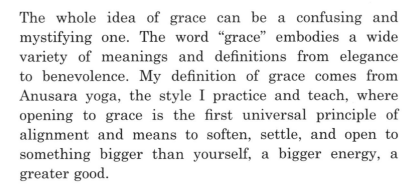

This experience of living larger—
and being truer to your authentic self—
is opening to grace.

The whole idea of grace can be a confusing and mystifying one. The word "grace" embodies a wide variety of meanings and definitions from elegance to benevolence. My definition of grace comes from Anusara yoga, the style I practice and teach, where opening to grace is the first universal principle of alignment and means to soften, settle, and open to something bigger than yourself, a bigger energy, a greater good.

1

I had the privilege of leading a yoga retreat on the Osa Peninsula in Costa Rica, an absolutely beautiful place where we stayed at a remote ecotourist resort. We slept in yurt huts in the jungle, close enough to the beach to hear the ocean waves moving in and out and the howler monkeys roar (and I mean roar) at dawn every day. The proprietors told us the monkeys are only about the size of a small dog and harmless—their "howling" is their way of expressing their need to guard their territory. Still, the first morning I heard one, I thought King Kong was in our tent! In fact, the roar of these "harmless" little monkeys is so loud and terrifying that they used them for the sound effects of T. Rex in the movie Jurassic Park!

In addition to the noisy monkeys, outdoor showers, treks in the river, and the challenge of surfing all made Costa Rica quite an adventure. All eighteen of the participants on the retreat were open to the fresh possibilities this unique experience could provide. As with most retreats I lead, everyone seemed to be going through some kind of transition.

One of the participants, Wendi, was suffering the loss of her husband a couple of years earlier and hadn't been able to move beyond her grief. We noticed the first couple of days she was exceedingly quiet and almost withdrawn. By day three, however, she was talking and even smiling a bit, and by day four we could hardly shut the woman up! But what we really noticed was her absolute transformation. Not only in her yoga practice, trying poses she'd never attempted, like handstands and arm balances, but in every expression of her being! Suddenly, she was laughing, engaging, and fully participating in the adventure. She even signed up for the snorkeling trip, which was particularly significant because of her expressed phobia of water.

Wendi truly opened to grace in Costa Rica. And she continued her daily practice after her return. A month later, she started looking for property to build her dream home and retire in the mountains. Wendi had transformed her life from the inability to let go of the past with her husband to opening to the possibilities of her life and was able to move forward into her lifelong dream of becoming a mountain woman.

Fortunately, you don't have to go to Costa Rica to open to grace! (Even though Costa Rica is a great place to visit.) You can do it every day, no matter where you are. In that truth lies the power of this simple daily practice.

> By taking half an hour—or less—to focus on your deepest intentions through deep breathing, yoga poses, meditation, and journaling, you open to grace.

And almost immediately you will begin to receive all kinds of ideas, insights, and revelations—including things you already knew but may have forgotten.

When you open to grace, everything changes, because you change. Opportunities abound when you change because you can:

**Open to all the possibilities, opportunities, and potential.**
What you focus on expands. So when you focus on what you didn't do, don't have, and didn't get, you get more of the same. When you focus on the good, the options, the possibilities, you get more of that. It is the simple law of attraction. And you have to be awake, aware, and open to all the potential in order to experience it.

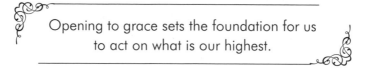

> We open to grace with a fullness inside,
> not by over-efforting, but by allowing it all
> to unfold in divine time.

**Claim your highest.**
You need to claim your highest first. Your highest joy, highest good, highest aspiration. What is most important? What is the priority? What is biggest? What holds the most passion and excitement—and maybe even the most discomfort for you? What do you want more of in your life? We easily talk about our priorities, but life so often gets in the way.

> Opening to grace sets the foundation for us
> to act on what is our highest.

**Live inside your heart instead of your head.**
Living in your head feeds the habit of comparing yourself to others, analyzing why you did or did not do something,

and second-guessing the decisions you make. It often means living by a set of rules and expectations that are not even your own. Living in your heart gives you time and energy to do things that have true meaning for you by observing, listening, and feeling your heart's desire. What you eat, how you work, who you live with, and how you spend your leisure time can all be based on your own longing.

> You are your most authentic—
> and therefore most powerful—
> when you open to grace by living in your heart.

Oriah Mountain Dreamer writes about living in your heart beautifully in her poem, *"The Invitation."* Here is an excerpt:

> *"It doesn't interest me what you do for a living.*
> *I want to know what you ache for and if you*
> *dare to dream of meeting your heart's longing..."*

**Stay in the flow.**
In the flow we ride the waves of pulsation, the ups and downs, the dark and light, the easy and difficult in our lives. In the flow we stay the course no matter how hard or challenging or uncomfortable things get. The flow means remembering you are part of something bigger: a community, cause, relationship, or project. The flow allows us to connect to something bigger and more meaningful than just ourselves. Ironically, we often turn to separation when we need connection the most.

Opening to grace helps us connect
and stay in the flow.

**Practice presence.**
Nothing is more important or significant than right here, right now. It is really all we have. We can spend so much time ruminating on the past, questioning, analyzing, and berating ourselves even to the point of depression. And we can agonize about the future, experiencing "approach fears," creating huge amounts of anxiety by making something really big, bad, and ugly out of what is simply unknown.

We also can spend our time fantasizing about how we want a situation to be and distract ourselves with shopping, food, alcohol, drugs, and sex to keep us someplace other than the present. These habits and even addictions force us to miss the here and now, the grace of the present moment, whatever it might offer.

In opening to grace we gain
richness and depth by experiencing
our lives moment to moment,
no matter what situation presents itself.

**Remember.**
Grace is not a state to be achieved, but rather a process—a practice—to be uncovered every day. Grace allows us to remember who we really are, our true nature, and our essential selves.

We are more than our roles as mothers and fathers, wives and husbands, teachers and caretakers. We are individuals with thoughts and feelings and needs and desires and dreams and passions and ideas and gifts. I am not just a yoga teacher or a speaker or a writer or a nurse or a lifestyle coach—I am all of those things and something deeper besides.

I used to think I wanted to do one thing and do it really well—to put in the ten thousand hours of practice necessary to achieve expertise and even "genius" in a single area like Babe Ruth or Bach, as Malcolm Gladwell described in his book *Outliers*. But intense focus on a single subject is not my true nature. I am happiest and most passionate and energetic with a variety of challenges. The unusual mix of high-risk multitasking demands that face an emergency room nurse daily is the reason I was able to function so well in my twenty-plus years working there.

Today, I open to grace and to the fact that as much as I admire people who have achieved these things and value what I've learned through them, I may never be a yoga guru, a master speaker, or a prolific writer. At the same time, I am a little of all of them. I am this *and* that. And sometimes that breadth of experience allows me to connect with people in a way I couldn't with a single focus. It can be easy to look at others we admire and forget the gifts we bring by being who we are and owning what we already have, know and do.

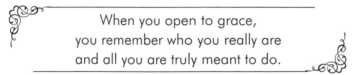

When you open to grace,
you remember who you really are
and all you are truly meant to do.

**Trust.**

Trust is the confidence and faith that everything is going to work out for the greater good, even if you can't possibly see how in the sometimes stressful and even frightening present moment. When you trust that you are loved, supported, and taken care of, when you trust that you are led by divine guidance, then you only need to pay attention and listen. When you trust that safety exists in the world, even in times that cause you to question everything, especially yourself, then you free yourself to function with all the potential that exists for you.

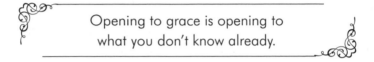

Opening to grace is opening to
what you don't know already.

Trust means embracing faith over fear—not the kind of blind faith in which you believe everything you hear and live in denial about what is happening, but an overall confidence that you ultimately will be all right because you are resilient, resourceful, and totally capable of getting to the other side of the situation, no matter what. Emerson said, *"When we exercise self-trust, new powers will appear."* What a beautiful expression of opening to grace.

**Let go.**

Letting go does not have to mean giving up or giving in, but rather releasing the need to control and struggle with the outcome of a situation. When you let go of the need to orchestrate what is best for someone or something else, you release the emotional tension around an issue. You agree to disagree. You let go of the need to know by letting go of the how.

> When you open to grace,
> you let go of a particular end result or path
> for achieving your goals and
> allow the experience to unfold.

Along with letting go of a particular outcome comes the willingness to let go of something when it doesn't work out. The most successful people in the world have a lot of different attributes in common, but one I am fascinated with is their willingness to make a mistake. They are not afraid to take risks, make lots of mistakes, and then get it right. They let go of the fact that something was a bad idea, poorly executed, a long shot, not researched well enough—or maybe they don't even know why it didn't work. They just move on. They are willing to fall down seven times and get up eight.

**Look for the good first.**
Something good exists in every situation, even if we can't always see it while we are in it. We can discover a lesson, a perspective, or a contrast available with even the most difficult of our experiences if we are willing to flip our perspective to the positive.

We open to grace when we open to the possibilities of what can be gained from an experience by looking for the good first.

9

Before I practiced yoga, I suffered numerous overuse injuries, from patella tendonitis from running to a torn hamstring from kick-boxing. I was deeply depressed about each of them, unable to work my stress off with my normal vigorous exercise routine. Although injuries are still difficult, I realized a recent shoulder injury gave me the opportunity to slow down and be more conscious of my body alignment, as well as appreciate all the times when I am healthy.

With any experience that feels negative or bad, we have the option of being the victim and asking, *"Why is this happening to me?"* or becoming empowered by asking, *"What good can I learn from this?"*

Sometimes looking for the good requires us to take a step back to get a different perspective. We can do this by practicing gratitude. Too often we focus on everything we don't have, when instead we can choose to focus on abundance and experience a feeling of gratitude for our many blessings. Oprah created widespread awareness of this alternative with the idea of creating a daily gratitude list—and, granted, she's got plenty to be grateful for—but by starting and ending our day focusing on gratitude, we can all experience a shift in perspective. Gratitude requires us to look for the good first, before the dragons of fear and worry sneak in.

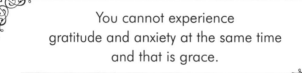

You cannot experience
gratitude and anxiety at the same time
and that is grace.

**Practice beginner's mind.**
Zen Master Shunryu Suzuki said, *"In the beginner's mind there are many possibilities, but in the expert's there are few."* When you view yourself as an expert, you are limiting yourself by claiming: *"I know that."* The Zen Buddhist concept of "beginner's mind" refers to having an attitude of openness, eagerness, and lack of preconceptions when studying a subject, regardless of whether it's new to you or not.

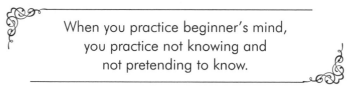

When you practice beginner's mind,
you practice not knowing and
not pretending to know.

Approaching anything with a beginner's mind allows you to focus more on the questions instead of the answers. The idea that *"I don't know"* leaves you open to receive and to maintain curiosity about whatever the newness is, instead of judging or criticizing. It also allows you to let go of "should-ing" on yourself with thoughts like *"I should know this already; this shouldn't take so long; I should be further along...."*

If I am taking a yoga class or being coached one-on-one, I open to grace by getting out of my own way and practicing beginner's mind. Even if I already know the material, I may not be practicing it, and it is much more interesting to listen with curiosity than superiority. The next time you read familiar information about a healthy lifestyle—those all-important basics of diet, exercise, or sleep—and find yourself thinking, *"I know that,"* try practicing your beginner's mind by staying curious and playful and asking, *"Why aren't I doing that?"* or *"What would it look like in my life if I did change some things?"*

## Forgive.

Nothing throws up more limits in our lives than holding onto resentments and anger about past events. Forgiving means surrendering to what actually was and your lack of the ability to make it any different, instead of holding on to the intense emotional charge around how you wanted it to be. When you forgive yourself for not knowing any better and forgive the person who has hurt you because he or she didn't know any better either, you set yourself free.

Setting yourself free can be as simple as writing the person(s) a letter articulating what you are forgiving and including acknowledgement for any part you may have played in their behavior. You can also list the gifts and positive things they have done for you in your life. The most important step is to destroy the letter and allow the burning or shredding of the paper to symbolize the burning or shredding of your hurt.

Remember your forgiveness is for you, not the other person or people, and allows you to let go of any expectations you have of the person responding to your forgiveness. Forgiving doesn't mean forgetting, but it releases you from the torment and suffering.

> We must let go of the past
> to truly live in the present.
> Forgiving is mercy. It is freedom.
> It is grace.

**Practice patience.**
Plenty of grace comes with practicing patience. In today's world of instant gratification, with our warp-speed technology, we've learned to want and expect everything *now*.

Opening to grace allows us to let go of our often unrealistic timelines and consider the long-term effects of everything we are doing.

Patience has never been my particular virtue, and I have learned the hard way that most things in life take longer than I expect. When I had been practicing my *30 Days to Grace* program daily for two years, even though my life changed in amazing ways, I felt as if I should be further along, more insightful, and more successful with it. A wise colleague reminded me that if two years had been amazing, then what would four or six or eight years bring with continuing my daily discipline?

Opening to grace on a daily basis
changes our days,
but opening to grace over a lifetime
transforms our lives.

Let's get started by creating your intention.

# CHAPTER 2

# CREATE YOUR INTENTION

*"Intention creates your reality."*
—Wayne Dyer

We open to grace to open ourselves to life's possibilities, and we create our intention to determine what sort of possibilities will present themselves. Your intention is your vision for your life. This vision is a force in your heart, full of power and passion that cannot be seen but can be heard and felt from within. Your intention is your ultimate goal, with a direction, an attitude, and an energy you want to cultivate in yourself and in your life.

> Creating your intention is very exciting because it is the beginning of something bigger, something more, something really important that you want to attract into your life.

You decide what it is you want to focus on for the next thirty days of your daily practice. You choose something meaningful to you in an area of your life where you want a change or a shift to occur.

Rhonda Britton, author of *Fearless Living*, said, *"When our intentions guide us, life is no longer a series of doubts and moments of questioning. Instead, when we take actions based on our intentions, we become more focused and have more integrity."* The whole idea of creating an intention and then focusing on it daily is to aid you in staying open to rich ideas, ah-ha moments, insights, remembrances, thoughts, and feelings that come up and then acting on them.

The area that proves most meaningful for you may well be one where you experience some resistance or discomfort—a part of your life that you are currently not dealing with in the way you truly want.

The Wheel of Intention pictured on the next page can be useful for helping narrow down the area of focus for your intention. The Wheel divides our lives into eight different categories. As you look at the Wheel, ask yourself, *"Where in my life do I want to create more awareness, more love, more energy, and more meaning?"*

Once you've selected a specific area of focus from the Wheel, you can create your intention statement, consciously stating what you want to create in that chosen category of your life.

Always write your intention statement in the affirmative, as if it is already happening. You do not want to limit yourself, so the intention statement itself should be quite general, even though the category it addresses will be very specific.

To help you get started, I've offered an explanation of each category on the Wheel of Intention with examples of intention statements:

## WHEEL OF INTENTION

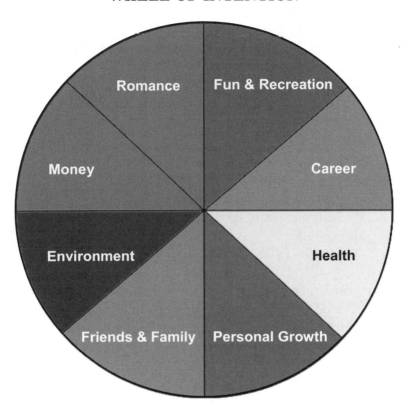

**Fun and Recreation** are the things that bring you joy—your hobbies, sources of entertainment, and interests.

Examples of intention statements:
*I love my boat.*
*I enjoy playing tennis.*
*I learn how to play the piano.*
*I create a new adventure every day.*
*I travel to exotic places.*

**Career** covers anything associated with work, including volunteer work.
*I attract the perfect position.*
*I write my book with ease, rhythm, and flow.*
*I do meaningful work in the world.*
*I embrace my new marketing plan.*
*I beat my quarterly goals.*

**Health** encompasses your physical, emotional, mental, and spiritual health.
*I take good care of my physical body.*
*I embrace my spiritual path.*
*My body is strong and healing.*
*I am healthy.*
*My emotional needs are met.*

**Personal Growth** includes any learning, expanding, or personal development that enriches your life, such as taking a course, finishing your degree, attending a weekend retreat, or receiving coaching or therapy.
*I fully engage in my education.*
*I embrace new patterns of behavior.*
*I am in a learn-and-serve state of mind.*
*I stabilize my mental health.*
*I move through my day with strength and courage.*

**Friends and Family** includes your children, parents, extended family, and friends.
*I communicate with my teenager.*
*I am surrounded by loving, supportive friends.*
*I embrace the differences between my sister*
*and myself.*
*I am a loving and attentive father.*
*I spend quality time with my girlfriends.*

**Physical Environment** is your home.
*I feel secure and safe in my home.*
*I surround myself with beauty.*
*I fully express myself in my home.*
*My space is clean and clear of clutter.*
*I create the perfect living space.*

**Finances** include anything to do with the money in your life—receiving, giving, and everything in between.
*Money is flowing into my life easily and effortlessly.*
*I enjoy my financial freedom.*
*I am debt free.*
*I live a comfortable lifestyle.*
*I generously share my abundance of wealth.*

**Romance** is the love relationship in your life that already exists or that you want to manifest.
*I attract the perfect partner into my life.*
*I connect with my partner on a deeper level.*
*I enjoy intimacy with my partner.*
*I fall in love with my husband all over again.*
*I create romance in my life every day.*

I encourage you to pick just one intention at a time to focus on so you don't get too overwhelmed or distracted.

An interesting phenomenon occurs when
you start focusing on an intention in
one specific area of your life:
It often overlaps into other areas.

For example, I had a client whose original intention was, *"I experience abundance in my finances."* In addition to bringing energy to her financial life, she soon realized that she was also experiencing abundance in her relationships and health.

If you are having difficulty choosing a category in order to create an intention statement, sometimes it helps to create one statement for each category and then select the most important one. For instance, here are eight possible statements created from each of the categories that might all suit one person:

1. *I travel to exotic places.*
2. *I write my book with ease, rhythm and flow.*
3. *I am healthy.*
4. *I move through my day with strength and courage.*
5. *I communicate with my teenagers.*
6. *I surround myself with beauty.*
7. *I enjoy financial abundance.*
8. *I attract the perfect partner.*

After you write down one intention statement for each category, you will need to select which of the statements represents your highest priority. Try starting with number one and comparing it with number two. The keeper from that pairing is then compared to number three—and so on until you've gone through all eight intentions. Now you know what your highest intention is, at least for today.

Don't over-think it too much. Setting your intention, like everything else, takes practice. We all have to start somewhere, and you can refine and retune your intentions as you go forward in the practice.

> Your intention needs to be open-ended, specific to a certain category, and meaningful to you.

This means no "should-ing" on yourself! Choose something you want, need, and are willing to focus on for the next thirty days. It can be a little scary or a subject that causes some discomfort or resistance, but it also needs to feel significant to you.

> Lisa, one of my life-coaching clients, really wanted to focus on her creativity and explore how she could bring her gifts to the world. Lisa also had some tax issues she knew she needed to deal with. She "should-ed" herself into writing her intention statement around her taxes, when what she really wanted to do was explore her creativity. Because her taxes didn't feel compelling to her, she continued to avoid them by avoiding her intention and daily practice altogether.

Writing your intention statement takes some practice in terms of where to be specific and where to be general.

> Bill, who came to see me for some transitional coaching, had the original intention statement, *"I am open to receive guidance in all areas of my life."* When I probed a little more with him,

I learned the biggest issue he wanted to address in his life was his finances. Instead of saying, *"I am open to,"* he could have said, *"I am receiving"* and have specified a particular area of his life.

That small change in wording may seem simple, but Bill first had to acknowledge he needed and wanted guidance specifically in his finances. He needed to own up to what was truly important to him and be willing to focus on it every day, for thirty minutes, for thirty days. Bill's revised intention statement was, *"I receive and follow guidance in my finances."* As a result of focusing on his intention, Bill got credit card counseling and created a plan to pay off his debt. He also slept better after taking some action.

Jan, one of my retreat participants, chose this intention: *"I am strategic with my energy in all areas of my life."* Although this was a good start, her intention statement did not address a specific category of her life. Because energy can refer to almost any area of life—money, time, physical endurance, love, or attention— she needed to be more specific. I asked her about where in her life she seemed to be losing her energy and experiencing the most pain. After a little exploring, she admitted feeling most overwhelmed and ineffective at work and refined her intention to, *"I am strategic with my energy at work."*

Every morning as Jan did her *30 Days to Grace* practice, she focused on how she could be strategic in her work. As she moved into her day, she began performing creative tasks, like writing and brainstorming, early in the morning when her energy level was high. Other tasks, such as paying bills, answering emails, and making follow-up calls, could be done later in the day since they didn't require as much energy. This restructuring of her work day resulted in a notable rise in productivity, and Jan began to enjoy her work more, now that she was using her energy more strategically.

What I didn't realize when I initially created this practice is how challenging it can be to create an intention. Your intention is really your personal reflective statement about yourself in an area of your life that is not working well.

> By creating an intention, you not only acknowledge you are having a problem, but you also take responsibility for finding the solution, even if it is uncomfortable.

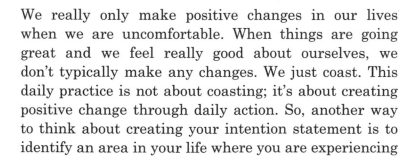

We really only make positive changes in our lives when we are uncomfortable. When things are going great and we feel really good about ourselves, we don't typically make any changes. We just coast. This daily practice is not about coasting; it's about creating positive change through daily action. So, another way to think about creating your intention statement is to identify an area in your life where you are experiencing discomfort or even pain and create your intention statement around that.

Steven Pressfield says in his book *The War of Art* that the greater the fear we experience, the more clear we can be that we have found our intended work, what is most important to us. If we didn't care about it so deeply, then we wouldn't feel so much anxiety about it.

> Expect to experience a little resistance and discomfort as you establish your intention—
> it is perfectly normal—
> but don't skip the important step of setting one.

Often, when I speak to groups, I hear people say they don't want to create an intention statement because they are afraid of picking the wrong one. Your intention statement is not written in stone. It is a starting point, and if you need to refine it or even change it altogether later, you absolutely can.

Abby, a successful publicist, came to see me because she still retained the proverbial weight gain from her second baby, who was now four years old. She also suffered from chronic fatigue, high blood pressure, and depression. Her husband had just lost his job, and Abby was feeling a lot of financial pressure.

After reviewing the Wheel of Intention, Abby recognized she had many areas not working well in her life, and said, *"I could pick an intention statement for every category!"* She settled on creating an intention in the area of health. Instead of limiting her focus to losing weight, the original reason she came to see me, her intention ended up being more open-ended: *"I embrace my physical body."* This broader intention statement encompassed her diet, exercise, sleep, and other issues that would directly affect her overall health, including her weight.

Creating your intention is so powerful because what we focus on expands. According to the law of attraction, when you focus on what you want in your life, you get more of it. Or, as the Buddha so simply stated, *"What we think, we become."*

I need to add a warning here about your intention statement, which is—be careful what you ask for! My very first intention statement was, *"I bring more yoga into every area of my life and bring more life into every area of my yoga."* Well, I got it! I started teaching more classes and private sessions, facilitating yoga retreats, and incorporating yoga into my speaking, writing, and coaching. I had indeed put more yoga into my life with this intention, and I had to find the right balance for integrating all of this exciting new yoga on my new path.

> Quite simply, living with intention means living on purpose—living consciously, living awake instead of asleep, living with the big picture in mind, with meaningful activity and consciously choosing your direction, personally and professionally.

Creating an intention and then witnessing first-hand the experience of manifesting desired change is an incredibly empowering experience, no matter how you approach it. The *30 Days to Grace* practice offers a manageable structure for bringing intention into your daily life.

After you create your intention, you are ready to move on to the practice.

# CHAPTER 3

# THE PRACTICE OVERVIEW

*"You must have a room, a certain hour or so a day,*
*where you don't know what was in the newspapers*
*that morning, you don't know who your friends are,*
*you don't know what you owe anybody,*
*you don't know what anybody owes you.*
*This is a place where you can simply experience and*
*bring forth what you are and what you might be."*
—Joseph Campbell

This daily practice is simple but not easy. The difficulty lies not in the practice itself, but in the discipline required to show up for yourself every day to do it. The more you practice, the more it becomes a part of your daily routine, and the easier it becomes.

There is great power in doing something daily. It gives you a measurement of your commitment, and every day you get to check in with yourself on physical, emotional, mental, and spiritual levels to remember what is most important. The practice runs for thirty days, so you have a starting and an ending point. Many say it takes twenty-one days of repetition to create a habit, and I know from experience that thirty days is enough time to experience real change and transformation.

A study from NASA backs up the thirty day theory. In the 1960's, NASA designed an experiment to determine the physiological and psychological effects of the disorientation astronauts would experience in the weightless environment of outer space.

To do this, NASA outfitted the astronauts with convex goggles, which flipped everything in their field of vision 180 degrees, so their world was literally turned upside down. The astronauts wore these special goggles 24 hours a day—even when they were asleep. As you can imagine, they initially suffered from significant stress and anxiety.

On the twenty-sixth day, one of the astronaut's world was turned right-side up again, even though he continued to wear the goggles. From days twenty-six to thirty, the same thing happened for each of the astronauts; their worlds turned right-side up.

What the scientists discovered is that after thirty days of this continuous stream of new input (as in a new intention), the astronauts' brains created neural connections to "rewire" their brains.

Fortunately, you do not have to wait the full thirty days to start noticing differences with your practice. As soon as a few days in, you will start to get out of your head and into your body, and you will also feel more comfortable and stronger not only while doing the practice, but also during the day as reflected by these two grace practitioners:

*"So far I have not missed a day. I am noticing that I am calmer and handling busy days with much more grace. I kind of glide from one activity to the other, keeping my concentration on what I am doing, prioritizing, and not fretting about fitting everything in."*

—Arna Caplan, day 7

*"The practice is having a strong effect on me. It is giving me the impetus to make other small changes that build on my mindfulness and serenity as well. I also noticed at least one person each day started a comment or conversation with me in places that I normally don't have that happen. I think I'm usually not very present at these places, but I have been more present than normal from the practice, and I think it attracts people's attention."*

—Paul Mezzacapo, day 7

The practice takes thirty minutes so you can experience the lasting effects of each activity, and it's a realistic amount of time to devote on a daily basis. Of course, you are welcome to extend any of the activities if you have more time and interest. If your time is short, you can select the activities that are calling you that day, for example, yoga and journaling.

> Even five minutes of the practice
> keeps you connected and focused on your
> intention and is better than nothing at all.

The practice is ideally done first thing in the morning, upon rising, for several reasons. First of all, the earlier in the day, the less possibility there will be of distractions and interruptions interfering with your practice. You also get to enjoy the benefits and set the tone for your entire day when you begin your day with intention. But most importantly, the first moments upon waking are when your subconscious mind is most active and your conscious mind is still sleepy.

The subconscious mind is so important to tap into because it is one million times more powerful as an information processor than the conscious mind. According to Bruce Lipton, PhD, scientist, and author of *Spontaneous Evolution*, 95 to 99 percent of our cognitive activity comes from the subconscious mind, and less than 5 percent is influenced or controlled by the conscious mind.

> When you access your subconscious mind through the various activities of the practice, all kinds of ideas, insights, and remembrances are revealed to you.

I am often asked whether doing this practice first thing in the morning means having to get up earlier. Unless you have another thirty minute activity you can skip in the morning, you will have to create the time for this one and get up earlier. Of course, I recommend you also go to bed thirty minutes earlier, which is another discipline we all need to practice, to get the seven to nine hours of sleep a night research has proven most of us require.

I can tell you unequivocally from my personal experience and from thousands of anecdotal stories from other practitioners that you cannot engage in this daily practice and remain the same. It is moving, mesmerizing, and magical. The longer you practice, the deeper you go and the more magic you experience.

So let's get started! Here is an overview of the practice with more detail in the chapters that follow.

**Daily Practice Preparation**
Have all of your equipment set up and ready to go in your sacred space, including covering and silencing any distracting electronics. If at all possible, do this the night before so that you aren't scrambling in the morning. Upon rising, dress in layers of comfortable clothing laid out the night before. Wash your face and brush your teeth, drink a glass of water and go directly to your sacred space (before coffee, checking email, or listening to the news).

Seat yourself on a blanket, block, yoga mat, or chair with your CD player or iPod in reach. I am being so specific about having everything ready to go because in the early hours it is easy to decide you "*just don't have time*" if you wait until the morning to set up.

**The CD**
The CD offers a full introduction to the practice and is then divided into two sections. The first section guides you through each activity with music and cues you to move on to the next activity with a chime. The second section consists of music only with cueing to move you to the next activity with a chime.

You can do the practice on your own without the CD, but most practitioners like the structure and the music it provides.

The activities of the thirty minute practice are done in a specific order to prepare your mind and body for concentrated focus on your intention.

In the first moments you open to grace by settling, grounding, and opening to something bigger than yourself. Repeat your intention out loud or to yourself. For example, *"I embrace my physical body."* Then, you spend five minutes in guided deep breathing to warm your body and calm your mind to prepare for the physical poses.

The next fifteen minutes are spent in guided yoga poses that cover a variety of standing poses, with balancing, core strengthening, and twists. Remember, this practice is not about the pose. It's about energy, called *prana* (Sanskrit for "vital life"), circulating through your body with various movements and breath. All of the poses can be modified and even done in a chair, according to your physical capabilities.

The five minute meditation that follows is to still your mind after the yoga poses. There are many forms of meditation, and for this daily practice you can focus on inquiry meditation by asking yourself, *"What is most important today for me to fulfill my intention?"*

During the last five minutes you will focus on your intention by journaling. This process includes writing down anything that comes to mind and committing it to the page. This unstructured and free-form writing can be done in the form of stories, lists, drawings, or even rants and raves. Choose the form that has the most meaning and relevance to you and write without censoring or judging.

These are the minimum times for each activity; if you want to go longer, you can always extend your time for any or all of them. As I've said previously, if you are limited and only have five or ten minutes, then practice for that amount of time.

I do want to emphasize it is the full thirty minutes daily that leads to real transformation, and like everything else in life, you will get out of this practice what you are willing to put into it, which means making the commitment.

## CHAPTER 4

# MAKE THE COMMITMENT

*"Start before you are ready.*
*Don't prepare, begin."*
—Steven Pressfield

It's great to have all of your equipment ready and available before you begin your practice, but it is not necessary. You can always get your yoga mat, the perfect journal, and a new outfit to practice in. The most important thing is to make the commitment and begin *now*.

As Goethe said, *"Until there is commitment, there is hesitancy."* You have to decide to make the commitment for yourself, for your family, for your deepest intention, to be all that you can be. Don't wait until "you feel like it"; you won't. Don't wait until "the time is right"; it never will be. Don't wait until "things slow down"; they aren't going to. Don't even wait until you create your sacred space described in Chapter 5.

This practice evolves as you evolve. It will become more sophisticated as you do. Begin today with a written contract to yourself.

# 30 DAYS TO GRACE CONTRACT

I, _____,

on _____

commit myself to the daily practice, *30 Days to Grace*,
for the next thirty days. I understand that the five activities
of this practice—opening to grace, deep breathing,
meditation, yoga poses, and journaling—are equally
important, and I honor myself and my commitment by
following through every day for the next thirty days.

I, _____, further understand
that this practice can create deep change, and with it can
come turbulence. I commit myself to excellent self-care
with optimal sleep, diet, exercise, and self-talk. Above
all, I commit to honoring myself and my own process for
the next thirty days.

Signature_____

Date_____

I realize that for every one person who embraces this practice daily, who gives himself or herself this gift every day, who experiences life-changing results, there are many who will not quite get to it. And there will be many great reasons why.

Doing anything daily requires a discipline, a commitment, a willingness to do it even when you are too tired, too busy, or just don't feel like it.

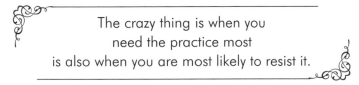

The crazy thing is when you
need the practice most
is also when you are most likely to resist it.

You can make all kinds of rationalizations and excuses.

So let's get all the *"Yeah, buts..."* out of the way. You cannot think of an excuse that I haven't heard already why you cannot do this practice.

*"Yeah, but I'm too tight to do yoga."*

Being flexible is not a prerequisite of yoga; it is a benefit. There are all kinds of different body types, and some people are naturally more flexible than others. I am not a naturally flexible person. I am a stiff person with a long history of tight hamstrings, low back pain, and multiple orthopedic injuries, including knees, ankles, feet, and shoulders. Yoga has helped my flexibility so much that I forget about all the pain I used to be in. I am only reminded when I skip a couple of days. The beauty of yoga is that you can start where you are and progress at your own pace.

*"Yeah, but I'm too old."*

Tell that to my ninety-three-year-old student who gave up square dancing because of her knees and took up yoga. She wishes she would have started practicing earlier—like in her seventies instead of her eighties. Isn't that fabulous?

I teach a group of seniors at a retirement community every Friday. They are the most enthusiastic, positive, and flexible group of people you could ever meet. Many of them walk to class with their mats in tow. Some stay in their chairs for class, but most get on the floor. They think I am there to inspire them, but the truth is, they inspire me.

*"Yeah, but I have so much going on right now—it's just not a good time."*

The more you have going on in your life—the busier and crazier you are—the more you need intention in your life.

Opening to grace helps you remember what you forget when you are stressed out and exhausted and helps you remember what is most important.

I know life can be busy and hectic, sometimes more so than others. This practice gives you more time in your day because you are more effective, more efficient, and more present in everything you do.

Life is constant change, transition, and adjustment—and you need the intention this practice cultivates to deal with it.

*"Yeah, but I'm concerned yoga does not fit in with my religious beliefs."*

This daily practice does not interfere with, but enhances and deepens your religious practice. Sadhguru, a yogi and profound mystic of our times, puts it simply:

> *"Yoga is a technology.*
> *Whatever religion you are,*
> *if you learn to use it, it will work for you.*
> *If you do not learn to use it, it will not work for you."*

*"Yeah, but I don't have enough time to do this in the morning."*

If you are absolutely not a morning person and are not going to get up thirty minutes earlier to do your practice first thing, then you can practice in the middle or at the end of the day. You can use it as a reflection time instead of setting the tone for your day and you may want to follow the restorative practice poses in Chapter 8. It is still very valuable—and if this is the only way you can get it in, then it is much better than not doing it at all.

Linda likes to practice right before going to bed as a perfect way to slough off the tensions and extra baggage of the day. She says the breathing and meditation are deeply relaxing and help her move from all the noise of the day to focus on her intentions. She goes to bed after journaling with her intentions fresh in her my mind. Sleeping much more restfully, she doesn't wake with stiff muscles—and even more interestingly, her dreams are more vivid and in color!

*"Yeah, but I already go to a yoga class twice a week."*
This practice is not just about the yoga poses. It is about five different disciplines and thirty minutes of focused energy on one intention. This practice can be an adjunct to your normal yoga classes or workouts.

Even though it's not just about the poses, it will make you stronger in virtually every area of your body; it will improve your yoga, your workouts, and your strength and flexibility.

*"Yeah, but I don't know how to meditate."*
That is exactly why I call it a practice! Because we all have to practice anything in order to get better at it. Meditation is something you have to experience in order to learn.

These five minutes will be devoted to asking yourself specific questions. The mind has more than sixty thousand thoughts a day, and meditation is about temporarily letting all of those thoughts go.

*"Yeah, but I'm not very good at doing anything in a regimen."*
One of the more powerful aspects of this practice is that it proves you can be disciplined, regimented, and consistent if you choose to be.

If life happens, if you miss a day, then you just pick up where you left off and continue with the thirty day program. If you resist systems and structure like I do, then this is a great opportunity to experience your day a little differently, full of intention.

*"Yeah, but I have a bad back."*

There are a few yoga poses that may be contraindicated with certain back injuries, especially those involving twisting. Every pose can be modified, as identified in Chapter 8. I have an eighty-something-year-old student who practies all the poses in her chair.

The biggest challenge about this practice is not actually doing the practice. It is getting to doing it. It is making the commitment to take thirty minutes for yourself, first thing in the morning, to start your day with focus, centering, grounding, and intention—every day. After years of practicing, I still have mornings when I get out of bed to practice and think I am too tired, don't have time, need a break, and blah, blah, blah...and I do it anyway.

The moment I sit down and take my first deep breath I remember this practice is more than just committing to the thirty minutes each day. It is about trust—in yourself, in the process, in the universe, your higher power, God, whatever you open your heart to. Trust that it is all working and the power of your intention is bigger than you can possibly imagine.

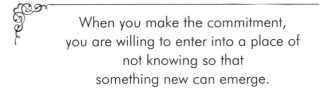

When you make the commitment,
you are willing to enter into a place of
not knowing so that
something new can emerge.

Now that you have made the commitment, you can create your sacred space.

# CHAPTER 5

# CREATE YOUR SACRED SPACE

*"Your sacred space is where you can
find yourself again and again."*
—Joseph Campbell

The idea of a sacred space has been around for a long time—you just may not know it by that name. By "sacred" I mean special, inviting, and intended for you. When we place aromatic candles around the bathtub and use bath salts and oils, we are creating a sacred space. When we use high thread count sheets and beautifully colored pillows in the bedroom, we are creating a sacred space.

We also create sacred space in our days by honoring our time and energy. When you choose to write or make sales calls in the morning, when your energy is highest, or when you choose not to answer the phone after 8:00 P.M. at night because of your deliberate early bed time, you are also creating sacred space for yourself.

This practice requires you to
hold a sacred contract with yourself
to create the space in your mind, day,
and life for a daily discipline.

Your space is sacred because it is the container you create to carry out this practice even when it is not convenient, easy, or you just don't feel like it.

43

Creating the sacred space in your mind is even more important than preparing the sacred physical space. It is giving yourself the permission and the responsibility to spend the first thirty minutes of every day on your deepest intention, what you have determined is most important to you. It is showing up for yourself in a way that may be unfamiliar.

To help create your sacred space, you could consider the first thirty days a sacred experiment, just to see what might happen if you focus on what you say matters most. Why not? By breaking through and changing old patterns of thinking, relating, and behaving, your days will be different because *you* will be different.

> It's important not only to create this sacred space initially, but also to maintain it by following through and honoring yourself for the full thirty days.

As with any new behavior, resistance will arise. There will always be a thousand reasons, rationalizations, and excuses for not practicing. *What if it doesn't work,* or, *what if it does?* Another likely deterrent is guilt over being selfish and self-centered for taking this time for yourself. (That is why I devoted Chapter 12 to this subject of resistance.)

After you make the emotional commitment to create your sacred space, creating the physical space is the next step—and so much easier! Even if you don't have a dedicated room, you can still create a sacred space in which to practice. It only needs to be large enough to accommodate your yoga mat and tall enough to extend your arms over your head for the yoga poses in the practice. It also needs to be as quiet and private as possible, where you are least likely to be interrupted or distracted.

The idea of a sacred space reminds me of one of my favorite essays by Virginia Woolf, *A Room of One's Own*. The title of the essay comes from Woolf's conception that a woman must have a room of her own if she is to write. The title also refers to any author's need for poetic license and the personal liberty to create art. The sacred space you create for your practice will give you the personal liberty to create your life!

Get creative with your space, just as you are getting creative with your life, and make changes that are meaningful and inspiring to you to really make it yours. Rearrange furniture, add color and texture with paint or artwork, and clear out anything not absolutely necessary.

> You symbolize clearing space and making room for your practice in your life by making room for it physically in your home.

When I determined the space for my practice, it felt very drab and unappealing to me, which was a great opportunity for resistance to creep in. An interior designer friend came over and went through hundreds of color palettes with me to determine the mood, energy, look, and feel of what I wanted to create. I finally settled on five different colors for my room (including purple), which I would never have picked out on my own but absolutely love now. Warning: Five colors in a small space is challenging and takes more "intention" than you may think when painting it.

> Think of this space as a place where you are creating beauty and make it pleasant and inviting.

I like to keep it simple and believe less is more, so keep in mind the space needs to symbolize clarity, peace, and grace as opposed to clutter, chaos, and busyness. You can create an altar with candles, flowers, meaningful forms, or pictures or have just one candle to light to symbolize the beginning of your daily practice. Whatever you do, make it special so that you look forward to spending time in your sacred space.

If you practice in your family room or another area of the house that has additional activities, I suggest you cover up the computer or television the night before to avoid distraction. Also, turn off the phone and email notification on your computer if you are in your office to avoid any other potential temptations.

Because my yoga room is part of a thoroughfare from our back patio to the kitchen, I put a decorative wall screen along the corridor to keep my space sacred, even when I am not practicing. You will also want to cover your practice supplies while they are not in use and roll your mat up so that children, cats, and dogs don't find a resting place on them.

I discovered animals are very attracted to the music and energy of the practice. After some trial and error,

I trained my golden retriever, Buck, to lie beside me when I was on my mat, instead of on top of me. I have another client whose four large cats join her in her daily practice. If your animals are too distracting for you to practice, then prevent them from coming into your sacred space as well.

You will need the following equipment, ready and available for your sacred space daily:

## Yoga Mat

A yoga mat is necessary to prevent slipping on a carpet, wood, or linoleum floor when you practice the yoga poses. You can buy a mat online and check out comparisons at the website yogamatreviews.net/premium-mats/ or go to your nearest sporting goods store.

You don't have to get a really expensive mat, but like most things, you get what you pay for. Two things to keep in mind are the thickness of the mat, especially if you have tender knees and want a little more cushion, and how much traction the mat can give you so you don't slip. It is preferable to be able to test one out before you buy it.

If you are modifying the yoga poses for a chair, then a mat is not necessary. You will need a chair without arms or wheels, and wood or metal is preferable so you can easily move from side to side on it.

You can also use additional props, such as a blanket to sit on and blocks and a strap to extend your reach in the yoga poses.

### CD Player or iPod
A CD player or iPod plays the instructions to guide you through the various activities. If you download the CD on your iPod, you will have it available wherever you go. Listening to the instructions or music through earphones can help your focus as well as create more quiet in your space at an early hour.

### A Journal and Pen
Buy a special journal dedicated only for your practice. You can go to your favorite bookstore or online (I like Pauper Press: peterpauper.com) and select a journal that really speaks to you. Or, you can create what Beth Sonorma, author of *Inspired Entrepreneur*, calls a visual journal with paint, collages, and cut-out phrases to personalize it just for you. Choose a favorite pen as well (I like purple) and use it only for your practice journal. These exclusive tools for writing help contribute to the sacred space you are creating.

Keeping everything together in your space is important so that your thirty minute practice isn't used up searching for various items. If you treat your space as sacred, you can train everyone else to treat it as sacred as well. As obvious as this sounds, announce to your family members what sacred really means: a special time and space off limits to everyone else.

Tell them you are not to be disturbed during your practice time for anything less pressing than the house being on fire!

 Over time families and roommates will learn to respect and support your practice because they see the positive change it brings to your life (and their lives).

Debbie lived in a small house with her two boys, ages five and eight, her husband, and a large dog. She cleared away an area in her home office for her practice. She had to train her family members that not only was this area sacred when she was practicing, but also when she wasn't. She instructed them that her mat, journal, pen, and CD player were to remain there at all times.

Debbie's dog was easily trained to stay out of her way during her practice. The boys and her husband were a different matter. They found countless reasons to interrupt her, from hunger to fighting to the disappearance of critical items. After the second week and countless reminders, she knew she had finally gotten through to them about her need for their support when her husband asked her one morning after she slept in, *"You are going to do your practice today, aren't you?"*

Creating this sacred space
may be your first claim of something
totally for yourself in a long time.

It is important symbolically as well as practically because you are standing up for yourself and saying, *"I am worth this time; I deserve this time; I give myself permission to take this time."* In the process of determining your own worth, the people you live with will determine it as well, just like Debbie's husband.

The first few days of creating your sacred space will be the most challenging. Taking thirty full minutes for yourself first thing in the morning every day is a new habit you are creating that affects not just your behavior, but also how you value yourself. The practice involves remembering and reclaiming yourself and your life with a dedicated sacredness.

You could begin your daily practice right now, if you have the CD. The following chapters offer you more information regarding each of the activities.

# CHAPTER 6

# DEEP BREATHING

*"When the breath wanders the mind also is unsteady.*
*But when the breath is calmed the mind too will be still,*
*and the yogi achieves long life."*

—Svatmarama, Hatha Yoga Pradipika

Deep breathing has incredible benefits that most of us do not appreciate. It helps calm your mind, warm your body, increase your lung capacity, and even burn more calories!

When you are focused on your breath, you open up channels of energy to stay present and more relaxed, not only during the practice, but also throughout the rest of your day when you are stuck in traffic, anxious in the dentist chair, or engaged in a difficult conversation.

Many Eastern cultures have long recognized the importance of deep breathing to cultivate a positive relationship between the body and the mind, one that results in a more tranquil state of being and a more resilient physiology.

Your nose is directly linked to your brain and nervous system, and the Indian yogis believe that many diseases are linked to disturbed nasal breathing.

Yoga, qi gong, and tai chi are such healthy practices in large part because they combine deep breathing and movement to support a steady central nervous response.

When I worked as an emergency room nurse, where tension was often high and patience short, I learned the power of taking a deep breath. It's unrealistic to ask someone to "relax" when they are in pain, anxious about what might be wrong with them, and have absolutely no control over their environment. Whether a patient was in hard labor, having chest pain or a panic attack, focusing on deep breathing always decreased their anxiety and de-escalated the situation.

I also practiced my own deep breathing in plenty of stressful situations while working in the emergency room. When a hysterical mother rushed into the emergency room and handed over her gray, limp, unresponsive baby, there was never a greater need for a deep breath! This gave me a brief pause to clear my mind of fear and anxiety so I could begin resuscitation efforts.

Most of the time we don't think about our breath since it is automatic.

> When you channel your energy
> to slow down, deepen, and add more rhythm
> to your breathing, the conscious mind calms down,
> and the subconscious mind becomes more alert
> with new insights, ideas, and perspectives.

The benefits of deep breathing are many including:

**Increases your energy level.**
A few rounds of deep breathing will provide a quick pick-me-up if you are feeling flat, tired, or stressed. You'll gain a dose of extra energy by supplying extra oxygen to your body.

**Improves brain function.**
Deep breathing oxygenates your blood and increases the blood flow to the brain for improved overall performance.

**Cleanses your body.**
Deep breathing removes stale air and impurities from your lungs and other areas of your body since 70 percent of your body's waste products are eliminated via your lungs. During poor breathing, less oxygen is available to your cells, which slows down the flow of blood carrying waste from the kidneys and lungs.

**Calms an agitated mind.**
Even a few minutes of focused deep breathing can calm a fearful, worried, or "over-thinking" mind. The ancient yogis believed that if you can regulate your breath, then you can control your mind.

**Activates the left and right sides of your brain.**
Alternate nostril breathing melts away imbalances between the left and right hemispheres of your brain. It calms your thinking by optimizing the analytical left brain and the creative right brain by focusing your breath on one nostril at a time.

**Relieves depression and anxiety.**
I witnessed great results with deep breathing exercises

at an intensive outpatient mental health program I taught at in Denver, Colorado. In a 2005 review and analysis of several studies, Richard Brown, MD, and Patricia Gerbarg, MD, reported that yogic deep breathing techniques were extremely effective in handling depression, anxiety, and stress-related disorders.

**Soothes your nervous system.**
When you focus on your breath and on deepening it, your brain registers this message and triggers the parasympathetic nervous system. You have effectively switched your nervous system from a stress response to a relaxation response.

**Improves sleep.**
A restless mind cannot relax. By relieving anxiety and calming both the mind and the nervous system, deep breathing promotes rest, relaxation, and sleep.

**Facilitates weight loss.**
Deep breathing delivers many of the same benefits as exercise, including facilitating weight loss. One basic measure of fitness is cardiovascular capacity, the amount of oxygen our heart and lungs can deliver to our cells. Deep breathing improves this capacity, thereby increasing the body's efficiency and ability to burn more calories.

**Stimulates the lymphatic system.**
Deep, rhythmic breathing expands the diaphragm muscle, the cone-shaped muscle under your lungs, expanding the lung's air pockets and massaging the lymphatic system. Deep breathing is the moderator of the exchange of blood flow carrying nutrients and

ample amounts of oxygen into the capillaries. A healthy lymphatic system carries away destructive toxins.

**Reduces pain.**
As I already mentioned, deep breathing is used a lot in the emergency room, as well as in the labor and delivery area of hospitals for pain management. Deep breathing not only reduces the anxiety we have with pain, but also releases endorphins, which is your body's natural painkiller.

**Reduces your risk of high blood pressure.**
Medical studies show a connection between high blood pressure and a shallow, fast breathing rate. Dr. Sheldon G. Sheps, a hypertension specialist at the Mayo Clinic says, *"Slow, deep breathing reduces activity in the part of the nervous system that controls blood pressure, which allows blood pressure to return to normal."*

**Helps you stay in the moment.**
When you focus on your breath, the inhalation and the exhalation, even if you don't change anything, you are focusing on the present moment. Focusing on your breath gives the wandering busy mind something to do, right here, right now.

**Gives space.**
Have you ever heard someone say, *"I don't have room to breathe!"*? The person could be referring to space or energy and a deep breath creates a little more of both.

Always begin your deep breathing by sitting up tall on a block, blanket, or chair, cross-legged or feet grounded on the floor, with your side bodies long and your shoulders draped on your back. It is optimal to breathe in and out of your nose because of the calming effect on your nervous system, so you may want to blow your nose before you begin to relieve any congestion. If you are unable to breathe through your nose, you can also inhale and exhale through your mouth.

Start by observing the natural rhythm of your breath without changing anything. Then start to deepen your regular breathing and move into the following three types of breathing instructed on the CD:

**Belly Breathing**
Place one hand on your belly, just below your navel. As you inhale through your nose, expand your belly as if you were blowing up a big balloon full of air until your lungs are filled to capacity. Pause for one second and then exhale slowly, smoothly, and completely, deflating the air out of your belly through your nose or mouth. Pause for one second and then start your round again and repeat four more times for a total of five breaths.

Belly breathing, also known as diaphragmatic breathing, is a simple exercise that helps you activate your diaphragm and breathe more deeply and slowly.

During diaphragmatic breathing you use less energy, require less oxygen, and breathe more easily. This breathing technique also strengthens your abdominal muscles and diaphragm.

**Three-Part Breathing**
Inhale through your nose in three parts, pausing at three different levels of the body, and exhale all the air

out in reverse order without pausing. Begin to inhale deeply through your nose to the level of your navel. Pause for one second. Draw in more breath and let your air expand to the level of your sternum. Pause for one second. Draw in the rest of your air and inhale to the level of your clavicle. Pause for one second. Now, exhale all the air out in reverse order through your nose or mouth, slowly without pausing. Repeat four more times for a total of five breaths.

The purpose of the three-part breath exercise is to help you unlearn the unhealthy pattern of taking in slow sips of breath through your nose or mouth. This breathing is deep and full. Three-part breathing ventilates all of the lobes in your lungs, allowing for an adequate exchange of oxygen and carbon dioxide, which in turn helps dispel anxiety and induce a state of calmness.

**Alternate Nostril Breathing**
This deep breathing may feel a little awkward initially, but it will become easier quickly with practice. Take your right hand and fold your index and middle fingers in, extending your right thumb and your right ring and right baby fingers. Bring your right thumb to your right nostril and lightly hold it there as you place your right ring finger lightly on your left nostril.

Start with an inhale on the left. Close the right nostril with your right thumb and inhale through the left nostril. Pause. Close the left nostril with your right ring finger and exhale through the right nostril. Pause. Inhale through your right nostril. Pause. Close the right nostril with your right thumb and exhale through the left nostril. Repeat four more rounds for a total of five breaths (on each side). If you get mixed up on the different sides, it is not a big deal. Just make sure not to hold both sides of your nostrils at once, so you can get air in and out!

Breathing in through your left nostril will access the right "feeling" hemisphere of your brain, and breathing in through your right nostril will access the left "thinking" hemisphere of your brain. Consciously alternating your breath between either nostril will allow you to activate and access your whole brain.

### *Additional Breathing Techniques*
These additional breathing techniques can be practiced after you are comfortable with the guided breathing exercises on the CD:

### Ujjayi Breathing
Ujjayi (pronounced "oo-jie"), which is popular in yoga classes, is created by toning the back of your throat to create a whispering sound. Inhale through your nose as you slightly constrict the back of your throat to create the whispering sound. Exhale through your nose, creating the same sound. Breathe smoothly and steadily, keeping the breath even in duration and intensity on the inhale and exhale.

Ujjayi breath is classified as a diaphragmatic breath. It can be used during your *asana* practice (yoga pose) as well as during meditation. Focusing on the actual breath and giving it a "voice" of its own helps enhance concentration and clears the mind of confusion or negative thinking.

During ujjayi breathing, the breath is long and continuous and the belly contracts inward, allowing the lungs to fill and empty completely. The friction of the air passing through the lungs and throat generates internal heat in ujjayi breathing.

Some yogis encourage their students to think of ujjayi breathing as a massage for their internal organs. As the core becomes warm from the inside, the body becomes prepared for the *asana* practice.

**4-7-8 Breathing**
Place the tip of your tongue just behind your upper front teeth and keep it there through the entire exercise. You will be exhaling through your mouth around your tongue. Exhale completely through your mouth, making a *whoosh* sound. Close your mouth and inhale quietly through your nose to a mental count of *four*. Hold your breath for a count of *seven*. Exhale completely through your mouth, making a *whoosh* sound to a count of *eight*. This is one breath. Then, inhale again and repeat the cycle three more times for a total of four breaths.

The absolute time you spend on each phase is not important, but the ratio of 4:7:8 is. If you have trouble holding your breath, speed the exercise up but keep to the ratio of 4:7:8 for the three phases. With practice, you can slow it all down and get used to inhaling and exhaling more and more deeply.

4-7-8 breathing is a natural tranquilizer for the nervous system. Although you cannot do it too frequently, Dr. Andrew Weil, well-known author and integrative medicine physician, advises not to do more than four breaths at one time for the first month of practice. You can extend it to eight breaths after that if you wish.

**Breath Counting**
To begin, count "one" to yourself as you exhale. During your second exhale, count "two" and so on up to "five." Then, begin a new cycle, counting "one" on the next exhalation. Never count higher than "five," and count only when you exhale. You will know your attention has wandered when you find yourself counting up to ten or twelve!

Breath counting is a deceptively simple technique used in Zen practice and keeps the mind focused on breathing, letting all other thoughts drift away. It is great to use during your meditation practice if you are experiencing busy or so-called "monkey" mind.

Everyone always has a favorite part of the practice, and it is most often the deep breathing. Although it is simple, the deep breathing is highly beneficial, and the positive results are evident immediately. Don't underestimate the power of the breath. Take advantage of the fact that it is the easiest activity of the practice to implement, no matter where you are.

Deep breathing brings an awareness to ourselves most of us are not used to, especially in stressful situations, when we tend to breathe in a very shallow and rapid manner or even hold our breath.

Jan was having frequent panic attacks in social situations and felt like she couldn't breathe. We practiced the belly breathing exercises to get her comfortable with the technique in a non-stressful setting. Then, she practiced deep breathing before she entered a social situation, which calmed her mind before going into it. She continued her deep breathing during her socializing, and although it was still stressful, she did not feel her familiar panic. Jan was able to maintain her deep breathing, not just in stressful situations, but also throughout her day.

There was a period in my life when I spent a lot of time in the dentist chair and developed a severe phobia of dentists. I learned to practice deep breathing on the drive to the dental office, in the waiting room, the whole time in the chair, and even on the way home, and it helped everything. My visits became much less traumatic, my requirement for numbing medication decreased, and even my dentist was more relaxed because I was more relaxed!

When I spoke to a group of top-producing insurance agents at a conference, I led them through a deep breathing exercise and they were amazed how different they felt after just five minutes. One excited man came up to me afterward and said, *"I breathed into places I never knew existed, and I feel great!"*

# CHAPTER 7

# THE HISTORY OF YOGA

*"When you are inspired by some great purpose,
some extraordinary project, all your thoughts
break their bonds; your mind transcends limitations,
your consciousness expands in every direction, and
you find yourself in a new, great,
and wonderful world."*

—Patanjali, author of *The Yoga Sutras*

This daily practice is not just about yoga, and yet it is all about yoga. Even though the physical postures are what most of us associate with yoga, it is not so much an exercise as it is a way of life. As yoga continues to gain popularity in the West, there is much to learn about its history and philosophy.

Yoga is an ancient practice based on a philosophical system with roots in India. It is thought to have started in 200 B.C. when Patanjali, a physician, Sanskrit scholar, grammarian, and yogi wrote *The Yoga Sutra of Patanjali*, generally accepted as the ultimate source book of classical yoga.

In this text, Patanjali presents the eight limbs of yoga, all of which help us develop self-awareness, completeness, and connection to something bigger than ourselves.

The eight limbs are:

1. **Yama:**     Restraints

2. **Niyama:**     Observances

3. **Asana:**     Postures

4. **Pranayama:**     Deep Breathing

5. **Pratyahara:**     Control of the Senses

6. **Dharana:**     Concentration and Awareness

7. **Dhyana:**     Meditation

8. **Samadhi:**     Oneness

The first two limbs, the **Yamas** and **Niyamas**, are fundamental ethical precepts that describe how to use our energy in relationship to others and ourselves.

1. **Yama:** Restraints
   Yama is the attitude we have toward people and things outside of ourselves.

   The Yamas represent the behaviors that control certain negative tendencies and are broken down into five characteristics:

   i. *Ahimsa*: Non-Harming
   *Ahimsa* means not to injure or show cruelty toward any creature or person. However, *ahimsa* is more than just a lack of violence. It means kindness, friendliness, and thoughtful consideration of other people and things. *Ahimsa* implies that we should adopt a considerate attitude and do no harm in every situation.

ii. *Satya*: Truthfulness
*Satya* means to speak the truth. In speaking the truth, we have to consider what we say, how we say it, when we say it, and how it could affect someone else. If speaking the truth has negative consequences for another, then it is sometimes better to say nothing at all. *Satya* should not come into conflict with our efforts to practice *ahimsa*.

iii. *Asteya*: Non-stealing
The practice of *asteya* implies not taking or misusing anything that has not been freely given, whether it is personal effects or information that someone entrusts to you. This prohibition includes using something for a different purpose than it was intended or beyond the time permitted by its owner. It also includes how we ask for someone else's time because demanding another's attention when it is not given freely is, in effect, stealing.

iv. *Brahmacharya*: Control
*Brahmacharya* specifically refers to abstinence from inappropriate sexual activity in order to cultivate relationships that foster our understanding of the highest truths. *Brahmacharya* does not necessarily imply celibacy, but it does mean practicing responsible behavior with our sexual energy.

v. *Aparigraha*: Non-Greed
*Aparigraha* means to take only what is necessary and not to act greedy. We should only take what we have earned. Collecting and hoarding things is a lack of faith in our ability to provide for our

65

own future. *Aparigraha* also implies letting go of our attachments to things and understanding that impermanence and change are the only constants.

2. **Niyama:** Observances
Niyamas are how we relate to ourselves inwardly. Niyamas refer to the attitudes that are necessary if we truly want to achieve health and deep balance within ourselves.

   i. *Sauca*: Purity
*Sauca* means outer and inner cleanliness. Outer cleanliness means keeping ourselves clean. Inner cleanliness entails healthy, free functioning of our bodily organs, as well as clarity of mind.

   ii. *Santosa*: Contentment
*Santosa* is modesty and the feeling of being content with what we have versus focusing on what we don't have. It means to be at peace even while experiencing life's difficulties and recognizing that life is a process of growth through all kinds of circumstances.

   iii. *Tapas*: Discipline
*Tapas* literally means "to heat the body." The heat we create with *tapas* has a cleansing effect, physically, and at other levels of our being. Tapas allows us to direct our energy to engage life enthusiastically and to achieve our ultimate goal of creating union with the Divine. It helps us burn up all the desires that stand in our way of this goal. Tapas is also paying attention to what we eat, our body posture, and our breathing patterns.

iv. *Svadhyaya*: Self-Study
Any activity that cultivates self-reflective consciousness can be considered *svadhyaya*. It means to find self-awareness intentionally in all our activities and efforts, even in accepting our limitations. Through this self-reflection we learn to be more centered and less reactive to unwanted and self-destructive tendencies.

v. *Isvarapranidhana*: Surrender
*Isvarapranidhana* is the recognition that the spiritual permeates everything and that through our attention we can attune ourselves to our purpose as partnering with the Creator.

3. **Asana:** Yoga Postures
Asana is the practice of the physical postures that most of us have in mind when we think of yoga. The practice of moving the body into postures has numerous benefits. Physically, asana creates strength, balance, endurance, and flexibility. Mentally, it increases focus and concentration. Emotionally, it relieves stress and anxiety. Spiritually, it creates a deeper connection between ourselves and the Divine.

4. **Pranayama:** Deep Breathing
Pranayama is measuring, controlling, and directing the breath. In our respiration process, we inhale oxygen into our body, going through our body systems in a form of energy to our different body parts. Then, we exhale carbon dioxide and take away the toxic wastes from our body.

> In the Yoga Sutra by Patanjali,
> the practices of pranayama and asana
> are considered the highest forms of purification
> and self-discipline for the
> mind and the body.

5. **Pratyahara:** Control of the Senses
   To practice pratyahara is to withdraw the senses from stimuli and attachment to external objects, with the goal of achieving internal peace. When our senses stop depending on outside things to stimulate them, we can concentrate without being distracted. Pratyahara occurs when we meditate because we are so absorbed in the meditation. When the mind is very focused, the senses follow and become extraordinarily sharp.

6. **Dharana:** Concentration and Awareness
   Dharana indicates immovable concentration of the mind on a single point of focus. Deep contemplation and reflection create the right conditions to keep our minds from wandering. Dharana helps us to stay in the flow of our lives with presence and peak performance.

7. **Dhyana:** Meditation
   Dhyana means "worship," or profound and abstract religious meditation. It is perfect contemplation and involves concentration upon a point of focus with the intention of knowing the truth about it. Meditation becomes our tool to see things clearly and perceive reality beyond the illusions that cloud our mind.

8. **Samadhi:** Oneness
   Samadhi means to "bring together," to merge, to feel as if you are one with the Divine. In the state of samadhi, the body and senses are at rest, as if asleep, yet the faculties of mind and reason are alert. Samadhi is sometimes referred to as total bliss, when all seems right with the world. We can get glimpses of samadhi during our daily practice and in life, but it is not a steady state.

The *30 Days to Grace* program incorporates all eight limbs of yoga, directly and indirectly. The yoga postures, deep breathing, and meditation all support the cultivation of the rest of the limbs: restraint, observance, control, concentration and awareness, and oneness.

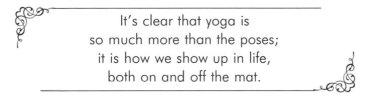

> It's clear that yoga is
> so much more than the poses;
> it is how we show up in life,
> both on and off the mat.

## Four Paths of Yoga
Over the centuries, four different main paths of yoga have developed: Karma, Jnana, Bhakti, and Raja.

*Karma Yoga* is the yoga of selfless action. Karma yogis express their oneness through everyday action, focusing on honesty, hard work, and service. This yoga purifies the heart by teaching us to act selflessly, without thought of gain or reward. By detaching ourselves from the fruits of our actions and offering them up to the Divine, we learn to let go of the ego.

*Jnana Yoga* (pronounced "nee-yan") is the yoga of knowledge. Jnana yogis use meditation and contemplation to discern the real from the unreal. This is the intellectual approach and considered to be the most difficult. It demands a sharp mind and unclouded intellect.

*Bhakti Yoga* (pronounced "bok-tee") is the yoga of devotion and love. Bhakti yogis seek to offer up all of their emotional energy to the Divine. This devotional love is often translated into songs or chanting.

*Raja Yoga* is the "royal" path to yoga and the most familiar in our Western context. Raja yogis use physical poses, breathing exercises, and meditation in their practice. Raja yoga encompasses most of the different styles of yoga, including Hatha, Kundalini, Ashtanga, Vinyasa, Bikram, and Anusara.

I practice and teach Anusara yoga, founded by John Friend in 1997. The word "Anusara" means "stepping into the flow of grace," and it has three components that differentiate it from other styles of yoga. It is alignment based, utilizing the five universal principles of alignment (UPA); it is grounded in the Tantric philosophy, which focuses on our innate goodness, teaching us always to look for the good first; it is community-centered, committed to inclusivity and building strong and supportive relationships.

Interestingly, I have seen many people turn to yoga when they are in search of more alignment, goodness, and a greater sense of community in their lives. That was certainly the case for me, as yoga has been a great source of healing for me physically, emotionally, spiritually, and mentally. After twenty-five years of teaching group fitness classes, ranging from kick-boxing to high-impact aerobics, I finally found yoga, or as I like to think of it, yoga found me.

Going through a painful divorce, without the will or constitution to get to the gym, I dragged myself to a yoga class, which in the past had no appeal since my goal was always to *"get my workout in."* After my initial class, I had a sense of peace and calm I had not known before but wanted to experience again. I was hooked.

During a time when everything was such an effort, yoga provided a safe place for me to experience ease, rhythm, and flow, literally and figuratively. After a couple of years of practicing regularly, I took my first teacher training and began to realize how much I really didn't know about yoga!

Yoga is a lifelong journey—
not just because of the different levels of a pose
we can achieve, but also because of the
different levels of ourselves
we uncover and reveal.

Yoga provides a means of coming home, of coming back to our authentic self because it requires and teaches us to focus on our own body, mind, and breath.

Our practice doesn't end when we roll up our mats. Without even thinking about it, we take this new sense of grounding and purpose and strength into the world, where everyone we encounter can benefit, including our children, spouse, coworkers, and the woman ahead of us in the supermarket line.

We need yoga now more than ever. Not in the sense that we all need to do a handstand in the middle of the room, but we have a great need for the presence, healing, and connection yoga provides.

> While there is so much uncertainty in virtually every area of our lives today, from healthcare to the economy to the environment, now is the perfect time to come back to our breath, our intention, and ourselves, with yoga.

Yoga is an empowering practice, whatever age you are. With all of us living longer, the idea of taking good care of ourselves has a much deeper meaning. I asked my yoga students at the senior center why they practice yoga, and they shared some interesting wisdom.

**Body**
> *"I do yoga for me. I reach places in my body and soul that I can only reach in yoga."*

Lucy is eighty-two and has severe osteoarthiritis, having endured several joint replacements in her knees and hips. She walks to class every week and always thanks me for a *"great workout."*

Regaining the flexibility we lose as we age is a huge benefit of yoga.

> Studies have shown that yoga also improves balance, core strength, lean muscle mass, and overall well-being, no matter how old you are.

I personally can speak to losing body fat, gaining half an inch in height, improving my sleep, and relieving my chronic low back pain after working years as an emergency room nurse.

## Mind

*"With yoga, my mood is much better, and it helps me with my everyday worries."*

Harriet, who is seventy-two, has a lot to worry about, with financial concerns and a son who is debilitated with diabetes and heart disease. She comes in pleasant and smiling, always asking about everyone else as if she doesn't have a care or concern in the world.

Everyone, including seniors, feels better mentally when they practice yoga. We get our minds off our ailments and limitations and focus on what we can do, so we become more accustomed to look for the good first. Dr. Andrew Weil wrote an article titled *"Yoga Promotes Weight Loss"* a couple of years ago, in which he revealed the results of a new study.

He found it isn't so much the poses and the stretching that provide yoga's weight-loss benefits, but rather the mindfulness associated with the practice.

Mindfulness includes greater consciousness of our bodies, promoting more mindful eating and a greater awareness of stress and how we cope with it.

### Spirit

*"Yoga allows my spirit to be open for the opportunity and grateful for all of my blessings."*

Jeanne, who is sixty-seven, takes care of her husband with endstage Alzheimer's and is trying to keep him at home for as long as she can. Being a fulltime caregiver, she can't always get to class, so she gives herself the gift of yoga every day with *30 Days to Grace*.

A huge benefit of yoga is the renewal of the spirit that comes every time you get on your mat. It is the movement of energy, or *prana*, that makes us feel whole and hopeful and gives us a different perspective.

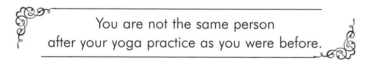

You are not the same person after your yoga practice as you were before.

I now understand fully why Judith Lasater, one of the nation's foremost yoga teachers and author of several yoga books, says, *"I practice for my students, I teach for myself."* Because I feel so strongly about what yoga has done for me in my own life, exposing more people to the power of yoga was my vision for creating *30 Days to Grace*.

# CHAPTER 8

# YOGA POSES

*"It must not be just your mind or even your body
that is doing the asana (yoga pose).
You must be in it. You must do asana with your soul.
How can you do asana with your soul?
We can only do it with the organ of the body
that is closest to the soul—the heart."*
—B.K.S. Iyengar

There is great value in a daily yoga practice. Every day you show up on your mat is a different experience because it depends on your energy level, mental attitude, and physical health. It can be a great benchmark for your progress and a great indicator for how the rest of your life is going as well.

If you are challenged in the balancing poses, maybe it's because there are areas of life in which you are feeling out of balance. If you are feeling tight and inflexible, there could be a current situation in which you might be behaving rigidly as well.

The yoga poses are a big part of the daily practice because physical movement is another way we focus on our intention. When you engage your muscles and hug the midline for stability, you fuel your intention with determination and courage.

When you extend your arms and legs out, you are reaching for what is most important to you with enthusiasm and trust.

All the poses can be modified to decrease or increase the intensity or can be eliminated completely, according to your current level of practice or physical injuries or challenges.

> Tightness or discomfort in your muscles
> is normal, but pain, especially in your joints,
> is a warning sign to back off immediately.

The yoga poses are divided into three groups. The first is the guided sequence on the CD and includes standing poses, with balances, twists, and backbends and can be done in the morning or during the day. The second group includes additional invigorating poses if you want to mix it up or go deeper, categorized by the body parts they concentrate on. The third group is a more restorative practice for reflection and relaxation in the evening or if your energy level is lower on a given day.

Whether you are practicing the invigorating poses or the restorative, remember that yoga is not about the pose. Yoga is about moving with your breath, and as long as you show up and aren't injuring yourself, you really can't do it wrong.

The English name is listed first, followed by the Sanskrit name.

# I. GUIDED SEQUENCE POSES

## Child's Pose: Balasana

### Alignment
- Knees apart on the outside of your rib cage
- Big toes together, hips over your heels
- Melt your heart toward the floor and place your forehead on the floor
- Stretch arms out in front of you, palms down
- On your inhale, lengthen your spine
- On your exhale, bring hips closer to your heels

### Modification Options
- Arms in front of you, under your forehead
- Forehead on a block
- Arms at your side, knees together, chest on thighs
- Use a bolster for support under your torso
- Sit in a chair and bend forward with arms on thighs

### Benefits
Opens the pelvic floor, hips, and back
Stretches ankles, knees, and hips
Calms the mind • Reduces stress
Decreases fatigue

# Cat-Cow Pose

## Alignment

- Start on all fours with wrists directly under your shoulders and knees directly under your hips

- Exhale and lengthen from your hips to your armpits

- Drop your head between your shoulders and round your back up to the sky as you look at your navel

- Inhale and root down with your hands as you spread your fingers to the floor

- Move your heart and belly toward the floor while you bring your shoulder blades onto your back and look up at the sky

## Modification Options

• Sit in chair with hands on thighs

• Round your back on the exhale and sway your back so your heart and ribs move forward on the inhale

### Benefits

Increases spinal flexibility

Opens lower back and abdominal cavity

Aids digestion

Opens the chest, throat, and shoulders

Increases circulation

Stimulates thyroid and parathyroid function

Reduces stress

Energizes the mind

Relieves mild depression and anxiety

# Downward Facing Dog:
# Adho Mukha Svanasana

## Alignment

- Start on all fours with your wrists directly under your shoulders and knees slightly behind your hips

- Place your hands so they are as wide as your outer shoulders and line up the crease of your wrist parallel to the front edge of your mat

- Spread your fingers wide

- Inhale and lengthen from your armpits to your hips

- Curl your toes under with feet inner hip distance apart and lift your hips up to the sky

- Soften the space between your shoulder blades and keep your lower back puffed up

- Hug the midline with forearms and shins (internally rotated)

- Straighten your arms and legs long and press your heels toward the floor

## Modification Options

• Keep your knees bent and bring your heels away from the floor

• Keep your knees on the floor

• Place your hands on a chair seat or back instead of the floor

### Benefits

Improves digestion

Relieves insomnia, menstrual and menopausal discomfort, and lower back pain

Strengthens arms, legs, and torso

Stretches palms, chest, back, hamstrings, calves

Energizes the body

Improves focus

Develops willpower

Stimulates the mind

Relieves stress and anxiety

# Forward Bend: Uttanasana

## Alignment

- Stand with your feet inner hip width apart, pointing straight ahead

- Fold forward over your legs

- Fingertips to the floor

- Weight distributed on all four corners of the feet, with more weight forward, on the balls of your feet

- Hug shins into the midline

- Press thighbones back into your hamstrings

- Widen your sitting bones laterally

- Let your face, neck, and shoulders relax

- Legs are fully engaged, with upper body relaxed

## Modification Options

• Bend your knees as much as necessary to reach your hands to the floor or blocks in front of you

• Use a chair instead of reaching for the floor

### Benefits

Strengthens feet, knees, and thighs

Stretches hamstrings and calves

Improves function of
digestive and reproductive systems

Opens the hips and groins

Stimulates the liver, kidneys,
and digestive system

Relieves menopausal discomfort, headache,
insomnia, and fatigue

Alleviates comfort for sinusitis

Soothes the nervous system

Relieves stress, anxiety, and mild depression

# Plank Pose: Chaturanga Dandasana

## Alignment

- Set the hands as for Downward Facing Dog

- Shoulders over your wrists

- Keep the arms straight but not locked

- Melt your heart between your shoulder blades

- Puff up your lower back

- Feet inner hip distance apart and legs engaged

- Heels push toward the back of the room

- Neck in line with your spine

- Hips no higher than your shoulders to make an even line with your torso

## Modification Options

- Knees on floor

- Forearms on floor

### Benefits
Strengthens the legs, buttocks, back, abdominals, shoulders, arms, and wrists

Improves circulation and digestion

Relieves fatigue

Energizes the body

Builds core strength

Improves concentration

Develops focus

## Cobra: Bhujangasana

## Alignment

- Lie on your belly and place your hands on the floor with fingertips at the level of your nipples
- Bend your elbows and keep them perpendicular to the floor
- Feet pointed straight back, inner hip distance apart
- Press the tops of your feet and all ten toenails into the floor
- Keep your legs engaged and parallel, hugging the midline
- Lengthen side bodies and draw your shoulder blades onto your back
- Bring your shoulders up and back as you lift your head and chest off the floor
- Keep shoulders back, neck back, ears back
- Keep your elbows bent so that the shoulders don't round forward
- Gaze forward and up

## Modification Options

• Place the elbows under the shoulders and extend the forearms forward on the floor, parallel to each other (sphinx pose)

• Sit in chair, arms on armrests, lengthen side bodies, and open your chest as you gaze toward the sky

**Benefits**

Improves posture

Stimulates the circulatory, digestive, and lymphatic systems

Opens the chest, shoulders, and throat

Lengthens the spine and increases spine flexibility

Strengthens the lower back, shoulders, and legs

Reduces fatigue

Energizes the mind

Relieves mild depression and anxiety

Reduces stress

## Crescent Lunge: Anjaneyasana

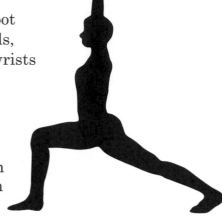

### Alignment

- Bring your front foot between your hands, in line with your wrists

- Heel up on your back foot

- Come to fingertips

- Front leg is bent in a deep lunge, thigh parallel to floor

- Knee comes no further forward than ankle and tracks over the little toe side of the foot

- Engage and lift your back thigh up, leg straight

- Hug the midline with your legs, by energetically drawing them toward each other

- Inhale to bring your torso up and hands to your hips

- Bring your waistline back and your tailbone down

- Lengthen your side bodies

- Extend your fully engaged arms over your head

- Move shoulder blades onto your back

- Gaze upward

## Modification Options

• Back knee stays on the floor

• Keep hands on hips

• Seated sideways in armless chair

### Benefits

Strengthens the arches, ankles,
knees, and thighs

Stretches the hips and shoulders

Opens the chest

Stimulates digestion

Increases muscular endurance

Builds mental focus

Develops willpower

Stimulates the mind

## Warrior II: Virabhadrasana II

### Alignment

- Take a wide stance
- Align the front heel with the arch of your back foot
- Front foot points straight forward
- Back foot is at a right angle, parallel with the back edge of your mat
- Front leg is bent in a deep lunge, thigh parallel to floor
- Knee comes no further forward than ankle and tracks over the little toe side of the foot
- Back leg is straight
- Keep torso perpendicular with the floor
- Engage the legs by hugging them toward each other
- Lift the back thigh up and back
- Extend arms in front and back of you
- Lengthen side bodies and bring shoulders on the backside
- Gaze over your middle front finger

## Modifications

• Shorter stance

• Hands on hips

• Edge of back foot at wall for support

• Seated sideways in armless chair

### Benefits

Strengthens the arches, ankles, knees, and thighs

Stretches the hips and shoulders

Broadens the chest

Increases lung capacity

Stimulates digestion and circulation

Enhances muscular endurance

Lengthens the spine

Builds focus

Develops willpower

Stimulates the mind

## Side Angle: Parsvakonasana

### Alignment
- Take a wide stance
- Align your front heel with the arch of your back foot
- Front foot points straight forward
- Back foot is at a right angle, parallel with the back edge of your mat
- Front leg is bent in a deep lunge, thigh parallel to floor
- Knee comes no further forward than ankle and tracks over the little toe side of the foot
- Back leg is straight
- Engage the legs by hugging them toward each other
- Lift your back thigh up and back
- Place bottom hand on the floor, outside your front foot
- Lengthen side bodies to open your top shoulder and back hip
- Move top shoulder back
- Extend top arm over your top ear, creating one long line from the tips of your fingers to the outside of your back foot
- Gaze toward the sky

## Modifications

- Bottom forearm on front thigh instead of floor

- Back hand on back hip

- Gaze straight ahead if you feel any strain in your neck

- Edge of back foot at wall for support

- Seated sideways in chair

### Benefits

Strengthens the ankles, calves, knees, and thighs

Opens hips and groins

Increases lung capacity

Lengthens the spine

Improves digestion

Improves balance

Builds focus

Develops willpower

Stimulates the circulatory and lymphatic systems

Stimulates the mind

Reduces stress

## Side-Angle Twist: Parsvakonasana

### Alignment

Same as Parsvakonasana plus:

- Engage abdominals for the twist

- Keep side bodies long

- Back foot stays flat on floor at a side angle parallel to the back of your mat

- Top hand comes to the inside of your front foot

- Twist torso and bottom hand extends to the sky

## Modification Options

- Back heel off the floor

- Back knee on the floor

- Keep top hand on hip instead of extending

- Gaze down

- Seated sideways in chair

**Benefits**

Strengthens the ankles, calves, knees, and thighs

Opens hips and groins

Increases lung capacity

Lengthens the spine

Improves digestion

Improves balance

Stimulates the circulatory and lymphatic systems

Builds focus

Develops willpower

Stimulates the mind

Reduces stress

## Tree Pose: Vrksasana

### Alignment

- Standing, firm up your left leg by engaging your left thigh

- Press your right foot, with toes pointing toward the floor, to the inside of your left thigh

- Press left thigh into your right foot

- Left thigh back and tailbone down to open your right hip

- Hands at heart center

- Extend straight engaged arms over your head, keeping your shoulder blades on your back

- Wave arms like branches in the wind (optional)

- Gaze is on a still point three feet in front of you, a little lower than eye level

**Modification Options**

• Right heel on the inside of your ankle with the toes resting on the floor as a "kickstand"

• Right foot on calf (not on knee)

• Keep hands at heart center or on your hips

• Place left hand on a wall for stability

• Hold or lean on a chair for stability

**Benefits**

Strengthens the arches, ankles, calves, and thighs

Lengthens the spine

Improves balance

Opens the shoulder, chest, thighs, and hips

Improves circulation

Calms the mind

Cultivates poise and focus

## Bridge Pose: Setu Banda Sarvangasana

### Alignment
- Lie on back
- Place feet flat on ground with knees bent and close enough to your hips for fingertips to brush your heels
- Feet are hip distance apart, parallel to each other
- Elbows to your side with palms facing each other in the air
- Lengthen side bodies
- Press shoulders and elbows to the floor
- Press your sitting bones to the floor to create a little arch in your lower back
- Ground firmly through the inner edges of your feet so your knees do not splay out
- Inhale and lift your hips to the sky
- Press down through the center of the back of your head, so your neck stays long, with your chin pointed to the sky
- Clasp your hands together underneath your lower back, roll your shoulders one at a time underneath you, and press your arms into the ground

## Modification Options

• Arms stay beside your torso

• Legs supported in a chair

### Benefits

Improves flexibility in spine and shoulders

Stimulates the nervous system

Aids digestion

Opens the chest, neck, and shoulders

Stimulates the thyroid and parathyroid glands

Increases lung capacity

Relieves menstrual and menopausal discomfort

Reduces fatigue

Energizes the mind

Relieves mild depression and anxiety

Reduces stress

## Supine Twist: Jathara Parivartanasana

### Alignment

- Bring your knees into your chest and hug your arms around your legs

- Release your arms and bend your knees at a right angle so your shins are parallel with the floor

- Keep knees and feet close together

- Press sitting bones to the floor to create a slight arch in the lower back

- Arms come to a T on either side with palms facing up

- Keeping both shoulders on the floor, bring your knees to the right while you gaze to the left

- Keeping both shoulders on the floor, bring your knees to the left while you gaze to the right

## Modification Options

• Keep the leg you are turning toward straight

• Keep your head and gaze directed straight up if you feel any strain in the neck

• Take your arms down closer toward your sides if they do not rest on the floor when extended, directly out from the shoulders

• Use a block or blanket under your knees for support

**Benefits**

Stretches spine and shoulders

Improves digestion and circulation

Strengthens lower back

Opens chest and hips

Relieves mild depression

Helps relieve stress and anxiety

## Final Resting Pose: Savasana

## Alignment

• Lie on your back and extend your legs in front of you

• With some space between your feet, allow your ankles to roll naturally to the outside

• Extend arms by your sides, palms up, with some space between your arms and ribs

• Rest on the center of the back of your head

• Relax your face, jaw, and neck

• Soften and surrender completely into the earth

## Modification Options

• Place a bolster or blanket under your knees for support and comfort

• Legs up the wall or on a chair for comfort

• Lie on your side or stomach for comfort

**Benefits**

Lowers blood pressure

Relaxes and rejuvenates the body

Reduces fatigue

Reduces stress, mild depression, anxiety

Reduces insomnia

Calms and centers the mind

# II. ADDITIONAL INVIGORATING POSES

## *HIP OPENERS*

### Half Pigeon: Eka Pada Rajakapotasana

## Alignment

- Start in Downward Facing Dog, then bend one knee, bring it forward, and place it on the ground out wide, near the same side hand

- Lower your back knee onto the ground with your leg extended straight behind you, without rolling it to the inside of your back leg

- Place your front foot near the opposite groin

- Point your front foot to make a straight line with the shin, then activate the ball of your foot

- Press your back foot into the floor for leverage

- Square your hips to the front by drawing your bent leg hip back and your straight leg hip forward

- Extend long from your hips out through your back leg

**Benefits**
Energizes the body

Opens the hip flexors, thighs, chest,
and shoulders

Improves circulation in
abdomen and lower back

Stimulates the digestive and
reproductive systems

Encourages healthy thyroid, parathyroid,
and adrenal function

Energizes the mind

Relieves mild depression and anxiety

Reduces stress

## Firelog: Agnistambhasana

## Alignment

- Sit cross-legged with your left foot under your right leg and your right leg on top of your left

- Right ankle is in the middle of your left thigh

- Engage both feet actively as if you were standing on them, flexing the toes back toward the shins

- Side bodies long and shoulders on your back

- Engage your inner thighs

- Press your right knee toward the floor

- For a deeper pose (only if your right knee is resting on your left foot), keep side bodies long and feet active, fold forward leading with your heart

## Modification Options

• Prop yourself up on one or more blankets if your knees are above your hips when you sit cross-legged

• Keep your left leg bent in front of you and place your right ankle on top of your left thigh

**Benefits**

Opens the hips and groins

Improves circulation in your abdomen and lower back

Stimulates the digestive and reproductive systems

Encourages healthy thyroid, parathyroid, and adrenal function

Energizes the mind

Relieves mild depression and anxiety

Reduces stress

## Garland: Malasana

### Alignment

- Stand with you feet a little wider than hip width apart, parallel to each other
- Squat down with your hips off the floor, keeping your heels on the floor
- Bring your hands into prayer position, with your elbows on the inside of your knees
- Elbows resist knees out as knees hug elbows in
- Root your tailbone down and extend up from the core of your pelvis to the crown of your head
- Ground actively through your feet into the floor
- Lengthen side bodies
- Anchor your heels to the floor
- Shoulders on your back
- Gaze is forward

## Modification Options

• Widen your stance

• Allow your toes to angle out to the sides

• Place a folded blanket under your heels if they
do not touch the floor

### Benefits

Increases circulation in digestion system

Opens the hips and groins

Relieves sciatica

Improves balance

Strengthens arches of the feet and ankles

Alleviates lower back pain

Helps relieve menstrual discomfort

Helps relieve constipation

Relieves stress, anxiety, and mild depression

Creates poise

Cultivates focus

# *BACKBENDS*

## Upward Facing Bow: Dhanurasana

### Alignment

- Lie on your belly

- Keep knees together as you bend them, reach back, and hold the tops of your feet or ankles from the outside

- Activate your feet by flexing the toes back toward your shins

- Rest your forehead on the floor

- Lengthen your side bodies as you bring your shoulders on your back

- Kick into your hands as you raise your torso and knees off the floor

- Only your belly stays on the floor

- Inhale and lengthen your side bodies and exhale and kick stronger into your hands

- Keep your knees together

- Gaze is forward and up, keeping the back of your neck long

## Modification Options

• Keep knees on the floor

• Use a strap to reach your feet

• Use a bolster or blanket under your torso for support

### Benefits

Stretches the ankles, calves, thighs, and spine

Strengthens the spine

Opens the chest and throat

Aids digestion

Energizes the body and mind

Relieves mild depression and anxiety

Reduces stress

## Camel: Ustrasana

### Alignment

- Come to your knees with thighs parallel to each other, inner hip distance apart

- Hands on your lower back, spread wide with fingertips toward the floor

- Press your feet actively into the floor behind you, with toes curled under and heels up

- Lengthen your side bodies to bring your shoulders on the backside and elbows closer together

- Bring your thighs back and tailbone down

- Round your back over an imaginary beach ball as you lift your heart to the sky and curl your shoulders back

- Pelvis comes forward, thighs stay back

- Neck stays long and in line with your spine

- Open your jaw slightly to keep your throat relaxed

- To take the pose deeper, reach back and place one hand on each heel

- Allow the head to go fully back as long as there is no strain

- Come back up with the head coming up last

- Bring your chin to your chest if you feel dizzy

## Modification Options

• Keep hands on lower back

• Use blocks on the outside of each ankle for hands

• Place a folded blanket under your knees and feet for extra padding

### Benefits

Stretches the thighs, torso, chest, shoulders, and throat

Strengthens the legs, pelvis, and lower back

Opens the hips and hip flexors

Aids digestion

Stimulates circulation

Increases spinal flexibility

Improves posture

Energizes the mind

Relieves mild depression and anxiety

Relieves stress

## Wheel: Urvhadanurasana

### Alignment

- Lie on your back with the same preparation as bridge pose

- Place feet flat on ground with knees bent and close enough to hips for fingertips to brush heels

- Feet are hip distance apart, parallel to each other

- Place hands on the outside of your ears with the fingers facing feet and hands wide apart, almost to the outer edges of your mat

- Lengthen side bodies

- Press shoulders and back of your head into the floor

- Press your sitting bones to the floor to create a little arch in your lower back

- Activate your hands by clawing the mat

- Inhale, lift your hips to the sky, come onto the top of your forehead, and pause

- Draw your shoulders onto your back again

- Press your hands and feet into the floor, straighten your arms and legs, and lift your head off the floor and your body into an arch

- Hollow your armpits back and bring your chest forward

- Hug the midline with your legs and keep feet parallel

- Hip bones are level with your bottom ribs
- Work to straighten your arms and draw your heart forward
- Work to straighten your legs and bring your thighs back
- To come out of the pose, bring your chin to chest and lower onto your shoulders, then all the way down

## Modification Options
- Work bridge pose instead
- Use blocks angled at the wall for hands to provide more height

### Benefits
Keeps the spine strong and supple

Stretches the wrists, forearms, shoulders, and spine

Opens the chest

Increases lung capacity

Strengthens the legs, buttocks, back, chest, shoulders, and wrists

Stimulates the lymphatic, digestive, and reproductive systems

Helps relieve infertility, osteoporosis, backache, and asthma

Promotes proper pituitary and thyroid function

Increases stamina

Energizes the mind

Relieves mild depression and anxiety

Reduces stress

## *BALANCING POSES*

### Half Moon: Ardha Chandrasana

**Alignment**
- Start in side angle pose
- Walk your back foot 12 inches closer to the front and place your top hand on your hip
- Place your bottom hand 10–12 inches in front of and to the outside of your front foot on your fingertips
- Engage your back leg with your toes flexed toward your shin
- Bend your front leg and transfer the weight to your front leg, lift your engaged back leg up and straight, with the hips stacked on top of each other
- Balance your weight on your front hand and front foot
- Front hand is directly under your shoulder
- Lengthen your tailbone down through standing leg
- When you find your balance, extend your top hand up to the sky and bring your gaze up

## Modification Options

- Use a block under your lower hand
- Keep your upper hand on your hip
- Have both hands on the floor
- Keep your gaze down or straight ahead

### Benefits

Improves circulation

Energizes the spine and lower back

Strengthens the arches, ankles, knees, and thighs

Stretches the hamstrings

Opens the chest and hips

Relieves menstrual discomfort and sciatica

Improves balance and coordination

Builds focus

Develops willpower

Stimulates the mind

Relieves stress

## Dancer: Natarajasana

### Alignment

- Stand in mountain pose, bend your right leg back, and hold the outside of your right foot with your right hand

- Engage muscles of the legs, especially above your right knee, and hug the midline with your thighs

- Extend your left arm to the sky

- Keep your knees together and touching

- Lengthen your tailbone down and extend from your pelvis through your legs

- Lengthen through both side bodies and keep your shoulders on your back

- Press into your right hand with your right foot and take your right leg back and up, keeping your knee hugging the midline

- Lengthen through both side bodies and keep your shoulders on your back

- Bend forward at your hip joint, keeping your hips level

- Extend from the core of your pelvis through the crown of your head

## Modification Options

• Use a strap to hold your right foot

• Keep your left hand on your hip

• Keep hips even and stay standing without moving your torso forward

**Benefits**

Helps reduce menstrual discomfort

Develops poise

Strengthens leg muscles and arches in the feet

Opens the chest and shoulders

Increases lung capacity

Tones the spine

Energizes the spirit

Relieves mild depression and anxiety

Reduces stress

## Warrior III: Virabhadrasana III

### Alignment

- Stand in Tadasana
- Front leg is bent in a deep lunge, thigh parallel to the floor
- Back leg is straight behind you and foot at 45 degrees (Warrior I pose)
- Hands at heart center
- Transfer the weight to your front leg and engage the muscles of both legs
- Straighten the front leg and lift the back leg off the floor
- Back knee and foot point directly toward the floor
- Even up your hips to square them toward the floor
- Extend arms straight in front of you, palms facing each other
- Keep both legs active and straight
- Lengthen from the core of your pelvis through your legs, arms, and the crown of your head

## Modifications

- Keep hands at heart center or extend them bchind you like an airplane

- Keep back foot on floor with front knee bent

### Benefits

Strengthens the feet, ankles, calves, knees, and thighs

Improves circulation

Enhances muscular endurance

Improves balance

Stretches the hip and groin

Builds focus

Develops willpower

## *INVERSIONS*

Inversions are poses in which your heart is positioned above your head. The benefits of inversions are experienced by shifting your body's relationship to gravity and include improving blood circulation, reducing irritation and agitation brought on by hormonal fluctuations, calming the nerves, relaxing the mind, renewing energy, and faster healing of respiratory issues because of the increased blood flow.

Downward dog and bridge pose are considered to be inversions and are included in the guided daily practice. For more advanced inversions, such as headstand, handstand, and shoulder stand, I highly recommend you initially experience them with a trained yoga instructor for the correct alignment to protect your spine and to provide you with support for balance.

# III. RESTORATIVE POSES

Restorative yoga is a therapeutic style of yoga that focuses on relaxation, renewal, effortlessness, and ease. Blankets, bolsters, straps, and walls can safely support your body in various postures passively. This practice soothes your nervous system, quiets your mind, and invites you to release deeply held tension by easing your body into surrender with the support of props.

Typically, restorative poses are sustained for longer periods of time, five to twenty minutes or as long as you are comfortable. The poses that follow can be done in your morning practice if you are feeling particularly tired or sore or in the evening for a more relaxing practice. You can also do these poses alone or altogether anytime during the day when you need to renew and restore.

The setup for these supported poses is important and will become more intuitive with practice. Adjust your props as necessary to be your most comfortable in each pose.

Ideally, for restorative yoga you will need at least two blocks, two or three blankets and/or a bolster, a strap (or necktie) at least four feet long, and an eye pillow (or a cloth to cover your eyes).

## Reclining Bound Angle:
## Supta Baddha Konasana

### Setup

- Bring the soles of your feet together and let your knees open and fall to either side

- Recline back on a bolster or blankets, allowing your knees to stay open, and rest them on blankets or blocks for support

- Relax your arms at your sides with palms up

- Make sure your head is supported and rests at least as high as your chest

- Allow your shoulders to melt on the bolster and open your chest and heart

- Close your eyes, feel the full support of the earth

### Benefits

Improves digestion and circulation

Promotes reproductive health

Opens the chest  ·  Reduces fatigue

Relieves headache  ·  Opens the hips

Relieves mild depression, stress, and anxiety

## Supported Forward Bend with Crossed Legs

### Setup

- Start in seated position with legs comfortably crossed
- Sit on the edge of one or more blankets so that your knees are lower than your hip points
- Position bolster or blankets piled high enough in front of you to put your forearms on the pile
- Rest your forehead on your folded arms
- You can also use a block under your forehead
- Close your eyes and melt into your blankets
- Change the cross of your legs halfway through

### Benefits

Calms the mind
Relieves stress and mild depression
Stretches the spine, shoulders, hamstrings
Stimulates the liver, kidneys, ovaries, and uterus
Improves digestion
Helps relieve the symptoms of menopause and menstrual discomfort
Soothes headache • Reduces fatigue

## Supported Child's Pose: Balasana

### Setup

- Sit on your shins, knees spread wide, with a bolster or blanket pile in front of you
- Your big toes are touching
- Lie forward, resting your body and one cheek on the bolster or blankets
- Your arms can rest forward or behind
- Close your eyes and surrender into the blanket or bolster
- Turn your head and rest on the other cheek halfway through

### Benefits

Opens the pelvic floor, hips, and lower back

Stretches ankles, knees, and hips

Opens the upper back

Calms the mind

Reduces stress

Decreases fatigue

## Supported Bridge:
## Salamba Setu Bandha Sarvangasana

### Setup
- Prepare for bridge pose
- Raise your hips and place a block or bolster long ways under your sacrum
- Slowly lower your body onto the bolster or block
- Let your arms rest down by your sides with palms turned up
- Keep knees bent or straighten them for comfort
- Close your eyes, let the block fully support you

### Benefits
Alleviates lower back and menstrual discomfort

Opens the heart, chest, neck, and spine

Increases circulation in digestive and reproductive organs

Stimulates pituitary, thyroid, and parathyroid gland function

Helps alleviate sciatica

Stimulates the nervous system

Reduces stress, mild depression, and anxiety

## Legs Up the Wall: Viparita Karani

### Setup

- Fold a blanket to support your hips and place the blanket against the wall

- Sit with your back to the blanket, knees together and hips as close to the wall as possible

- Swing your legs up the wall as you lie your head and torso down perpendicular to the wall

- Rest your heels on the wall with your sitting bones as close to the wall as comfortably possible

- Knees are straight but soft (not locked), or bend your knees and take them wide, placing the soles of your feet together

- Close your eyes and let the earth and wall support you

## Benefits

Regulates blood flow

Alleviates menstrual cramps

Relieves swollen ankles and varicose veins

Improves digestion

Restores tired feet or legs

Stretches the back of the neck, front torso,
and back of the legs

Relieves mild backache

Provides migraine and headache relief

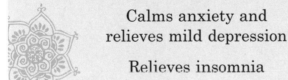

Calms anxiety and
relieves mild depression

Relieves insomnia

# CHAPTER 9

# MEDITATION

*"Meditation is the basis for all inner work.
It is the direct naked encounter with our own
awareness that shifts our understanding of
who we are and gives us the power to
stand firmly in our own center."*

— Sally Kempton, author of
*The Heart of Meditation*

Meditation is something of a mystery to most of us. We don't quite know how to do it or understand why we need to do it. I included meditation in the practice because it has great value, especially in today's busy, frenetic, and multitasking world. I want to simplify the practice of meditation for you and have you appreciate the complexities of it at the same time.

I love the way Sally Kempton breaks down meditation. She says it is both a state and a process. According to the Indian yogic system, we experience three "normal" states of consciousness: waking, dreaming, and deep sleep. Deeper than these, yet threading through them, is a fourth state we access in meditation. This meditative state is filled with power, intuitive wisdom, and joy, and it's always present (although often hidden).

Meditation typically involves sitting quietly with our spine erect and focusing inward. There are many different forms of meditative practice, and the technique itself is less important than the act of inward attention. It is the inward attention that calls forth the meditative state.

John Kabit Zin, author of *Wherever You Go, There You Are*, says it even more simply: *"Meditation is stopping and being present, that is all."* He says meditation is feeling the way you feel.

It's not about making your mind empty or still; it's about letting your mind be as it is and knowing it in this moment. That is possible for us all.

Most of my clients initially tell me they aren't very good at meditating or that they can't do it at all. Anyone, though, can be present to their breathing and their mind when they choose to be. Often, we are challenged at "being" because "doing" is much more familiar and comfortable, especially to people raised in the West.

> If you are willing to just "be,"
> even for five minutes, you can meditate—
> and the benefits are nothing short of amazing.

The following are proven physical benefits of meditation:

- PMS decreased by 57 percent

- Migraine headaches decreased notably

- Anxiety and depression reduced significantly

- Fewer missed work days due to illness

• Decreased symptoms of AIDS and cancer in patients with these diseases

• 75 percent of people with insomnia cured; 25 percent improved

• Patients with high blood pressure recovered comcompletely or improved

• Lower rate of hospitalization for all diseases, with an 87 percent lower rate of hospitalization for cardiovascular disease, 55 percent less hospitalization for cancer, and 87 percent less hospitalization for nervous system diseases

*(From research at Herbert Bensen's Mind-Body Institute, Harvard Medical School)*

• Chronic pain patients reduce their physician visits by 36%.
(The Clinical Journal of Pain, Volume 2, pages 305-310, 1991)

• 50% reduction in visits to a HMO after a relaxation-response based intervention.
(Behavioral Medicine, Volume 16, pages 165-173, 1990)

• Open heart surgery patients have fewer post-operative complications.
(Behavioral Medicine, Volume 5, pages 111-117, 1989)

• Infertile women have a 42% conception rate, a 38% take-home baby rate, and decreased levels of depression, anxiety, and anger.
(Journal of American Medical Women's Association. Volume 54, pages 196-8, 1999)

- Meditators who had been practicing meditation for more than five years were physiologically twelve years younger than their chronological age. (International Journal of Neuroscience, 16: 53-58, 1982). Journal of Psychology, 4: 206-218, 1976).

- 198 independent treatment outcomes found that meditation produced a significantly larger reduction in tobacco, alcohol, and illicit drug use than standard substance abuse treatments including counseling, pharmacological treatments, relaxation training, and Twelve-Step programs. (Alcoholism Treatment Quarterly, 11: 13-87, and International Journal of the Addictions, 26: 293-325, 1991).

A common question I get from my clients is, *"How long do I have to meditate to get the benefits?"* The best answer is the same as if they had asked how long they have to exercise to get the benefits. Ideally, for the rest of your life, for a minimum of 30 minutes a day.

Just like exercise,
the frequency of meditation
is more important than the duration;
even five minutes of meditation a day
is better than no minutes.

The practice allows time for five minutes, but you may find you want to sit longer as your mind is often just starting to reach the meditative state in that time.

When I am speaking to a large group and introduce the idea of meditation, I can see the immediate look of disdain in the audience. They are not just surprised but visibly uncomfortable and sometimes even borderline angry looking. I always have a brief thought that maybe they won't participate this time; maybe they will just sit there in resistance and mutiny. After they spend five minutes in stillness (as I often call it), I see their look of discomfort replaced with relief, relaxation, and even gratitude. They have discovered a new practice that brings them an immediate peace and calm most of them have not known before.

When you are willing to try meditation, many of the psychological benefits can be experienced almost immediately. This is, of course, after you let go of the notion that you need to do it "right." I have not only personally experienced many of these rewards, but I have also been witness to them in my students and clients:

- Greater capacity to withstand painful or negative emotions

- Increased positive emotions such as love, compassion, clarity, warmth, generosity

- More focus and clarity to the mind

- Increased capacity to understand and connect with others

- More lightness, humor, and balance

- Improved coping skills to deal with upset, grief, and fear

- Broader comprehension and improved ability to focus

- Increased creativity

- Greater orderliness of brain functioning

- Deeper level of relaxation

- Improved perception and memory

- Development of emotional intelligence

- Increased self-actualization

- Increased productivity

- Improved relations at work

- Increased relaxation and decreased stress

There are many different types of meditation, including guided, with or without music, mantras, and visualizations. Here are just a few different types of meditation you can try, including the guided and inquiry meditation instructed on the CD for the practice.

**Guided Meditation**
Guided meditation leads you into a state of meditation with the spoken word and often soft background music. Your guide literally walks you through the process, step by step. Guided meditations help you to imagine positive experiences vividly that represent, either directly or symbolically, whatever changes you wish to express in your life.

**Inquiry Meditation**
This meditation asks a specific question of ourselves. In the guided practice on the CD, the question is, *What do*

*I need most today to fulfill my intention?* You visualize yourself moving through your day with your intention, making the appropriate choices, carrying out your specific action steps. Be open to whatever comes up in your meditation time, and when your mind starts to wander (and it will), ask yourself again: *What do I need most today to fulfill my intention?* If you are practicing at the end of the day and are reflecting, you can ask yourself, *How did I fulfill my intention today?*

Some other examples of inquiries to ask could be:

*How can I love more deeply (myself or others)?*

*What is my highest good?*

*Where do I most need to devote my attention?*

## Concentrative Meditation

In concentrative meditation, you focus your attention on an object—whether it is your breath, a part of your body (such as your heart center), a candle flame or picture, a mantra, or a word. When your attention wanders, you bring it back, disregarding whatever else comes into your awareness. Concentrative meditation trains the mind to hold focus and calms the agitation that comes from repetitive thought.

## Loving Kindness Meditation

During this form of meditation you recite the same phrases that evoke the feelings of loving kindness toward yourself and cultivate inner states of spiritual feeling, like love, compassion, or peace. You begin with yourself because without loving yourself it is impossible to love others.

*May I be filled with loving kindness.*

*May I be well.*

*May I be peaceful and at ease.*

*May I be happy.*

You can also move on to expand your loving kindness to others:

*May he be filled with loving kindness.*

*May he be well.*

*May he be peaceful and at ease.*

*May he be happy.*

## Mantra Meditation
A mantra is a sound, syllable, word, or group of words considered capable of facilitating spiritual transformation. Mantras are chanted out loud or internally as objects of meditation. One of the most familiar mantras that many yoga classes begin with is "om" or "aum," which in simple terms means "all."

Another popular and easy mantra is the Soham mantra, which means, *"I am that"* or *"I am pure consciousness."* It has been called the universal mantra because its vibration is already a part of the breath, and everybody breathes. *Sooooo...* is the sound of inhalation, and *Hummmm...* is the sound of exhalation. With each inhalation breathe in "sooooooooo," and with each exhalation breathe out, "hummmmmm."

You can choose any word that has meaning for you for your mantra. For example, inhale the word *"let"* and exhale the word *"go."* You can also repeat the same word over and over, such as *"love," "peace,"* or *"calm"* on the inhale and the exhale.

### Mountain Meditation

Imagine you are sitting in the presence of a mountain. It may be a mountain you have seen or a mountain that simply appears in your imagination. Feel the strength, solidity, and rootedness of the mountain. Feel its vastness. Now, feel that you *are* the mountain. Within your own body, experience the stillness, the power, and the solidity of the mountain. Feel your own breath as the breath of the mountain. Your breath arises and subsides on its own, as though the mountain breathed.

### Preparing for Meditation

Take a seated position on the floor or in a chair, where your back can be erect. If possible, sit cross-legged in the easy posture and elevate your hips higher than your ankles on a blanket or block. You can also sit with your back against a wall or in a chair for comfort. If you sit in a chair, make sure your feet are firmly planted on the ground and your back is erect.

Lean forward and pull the skin away from your buttocks to sit forward on your sitting bones. Grow your side bodies long and move your shoulders on your back. Move your hips toward the back of the room or chair to preserve the natural curve of your back. The crown of your head lifts toward the ceiling while the chin is slightly lowered. Hands rest on your thighs, with palms up to be more receptive or down to be more grounded.

## During Meditation

In meditation, you keep coming back to your breath, your intention, the present moment. Some days are more challenging than others, as with everything else. As your various thoughts arise, you can label them *"Thinking"* then let them go and return to your stillness.

You are doing your meditation "right" by showing up and staying with it, even if your busy mind keeps trying to replay a previous conversation or plan your next meal. Jack Kornfield refers to this as training a puppy. He says we keep bringing the puppy (mind) back to where we want it to be. Again and again and again.

## After Meditation

After reading all the benefits of meditation, some people expect to experience immediate life-changing results. But the real power in meditation is the cumulative effect.

You are training your conscious mind
to be still and tapping into your
subconscious meditative mind to
access a deeper, richer state,
regardless of the outside conditions
that surround you.

The beautiful part about meditation is that you can do it anywhere, anytime, as long as you are willing. There are really no rules, and you can use your meditation techniques in virtually any situation.

When my dear friend Molly had open-heart surgery, she came out of surgery on a ventilator with a breathing tube down her throat and multiple lines of chest tubes, catheters, and wires connected to all parts of her body. They intentionally kept her sedation very light so she would breathe on her own and come off the ventilator as soon as possible. I was so surprised to watch her lie there, appearing so calm and relaxed like an angel, as if she were having a pleasant dream. After the breathing tube was removed, I asked her how she did it, and she softly mouthed, *"Meditation."* Of course! Molly has been meditating for years, and it only makes sense she would use this powerful practice during her hospitalization!

I have meditated for five minutes before giving a speech and for two hours sitting in an ashram with a group of two hundred people. What I am always amazed at is how every experience is so different and rewarding.

I return from my meditation with great insight or revelation—or not—but I always return more calm, clear, and conscious.

So can you.

# CHAPTER 10

# JOURNALING

*"We should write because writing brings
clarity and passion to the act of living.
Writing is sensual, experiential, grounding.
We should write because writing is good for the soul."*

—Julia Cameron, author of *The Artist's Way*
and *The Right to Write*

Julia Cameron brought the beautiful benefits of journaling to the forefront with her renowned book, *The Artist's Way*. She encourages a daily practice of writing morning pages for our own creative recovery. She recommends three full pages of writing by hand every day, first thing in the morning, to help find the true artist that resides in us all.

By comparison, the five minutes of journaling I ask you to do in this practice every day are minimal but very powerful. Journaling is one more important way to focus on and express your intention.

> Journaling is so valuable because you access
> different information in your subconscious mind
> when you commit something to the page,
> as opposed to thinking about it and processing it
> in your breathing, movement, and meditation.

If you don't consider yourself to be a "writer," it doesn't matter because you are not really writing; you are journaling, and it's only for you. There are no rules or formalities followed in journaling. It is writing as a stream of consciousness, with whatever comes up for you at the time.

Don't over-think this part of the practice. In fact, I invite you just to put the pen to your page and go, totally dismissing your internal editor and critic. You can make lists, word associations, random thoughts, poetry, and even rants or raves.

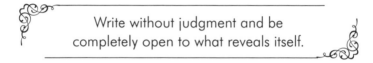

> Write without judgment and be completely open to what reveals itself.

Some of my grace practitioners are initially concerned that the ranting and raving they journal can sound like whining and negativity and, therefore, might be counter-productive. If your journaling focuses on any fear or hostility you may be harboring, isn't it great to get it out of your head and into your private journal before you start the rest of your day, instead of taking it out on your youngest child or the guy who cuts you off on the highway?

You won't always write rants and raves. You may create a written action plan or have a breakthrough idea in a relationship, project, or your health. But don't have high expectations. You are just expressing what is right here, right now, and that is all. No pressure, no rules—except that you do it without any attachment to the outcome.

As with all parts of the practice, we tend to like some activities more than others.

Before I created the *30 Days to Grace* CD in a studio, I enlisted a focus group to pilot my thirty minute program for thirty days with weekly check-ins. One of my grace practitioners was certain I had made an error in my timing, thinking I increased the meditation time and decreased the journaling time. To prove it, she timed each activity herself—and then confirmed both were indeed five minutes. Of course, she thought the journaling was shorter because she is a professional writer and liked that part the best.

Whether you consider yourself to be a writer or not, I encourage you to write by hand instead of using your computer. There is something more sacred, personal, and organic when you are using your favorite pen and touching the paper of your journal as opposed to entering it in electronically. I know you may be able to write faster on your computer, but that is not the point. This is one activity in your day you don't have to rush through. Write for the entire five minutes and let go of the idea that it is about how much you "produce" or how much insight you will gain. What matters most is that you showed up to do it.

Like any portion of the practice, journaling can evoke resistance. It's the same resistance we all face as writers and one I am very familiar with, the old *"I'm not good enough."* We think we don't know enough, aren't smart enough, don't have enough to say, and whatever else our critical minds can think of to keep us from writing.

It's important to remember no one in the world ever needs to read your journaling, not even you, if you choose not to.

> What your journaling does do is document the ideas, thoughts, concepts, beliefs, and opinions you have but may have forgotten.

Joan was a group fitness instructor for years and had a sporadic yoga practice before she committed to the *30 Days to Grace* program. She told me after the first week how much she loved it all—except the journaling. *"I'm just not a writer. In fact, I really hate to write!"* Joan had a difficult time in school with writing and carried that experience into her journaling part of the practice.

I encouraged her to follow through with the journaling, just for the thirty days as an experiment. She agreed, and, although it was still difficult for her, in the end she felt really good about it. In working through her resistance to her writing, Joan was also working through her resistance in other areas of her life as well.

The beauty of journaling after you have done your deep breathing, yoga poses, and meditation, especially first thing in the morning, is that you have primed your expressive pump. If you will just put your pen to paper and not think about perfecting or creating but simply let your hands start writing, you will be surprised by what will appear on the page. It takes practice to allow the journaling to lead you, but when you do so, it is magical!

Some ideas to help get you started are to journal about your experience of the practice that day—how you felt, what it was like (hard, easy, pleasant, or unpleasant), without judgment but with deep honesty. If you were wrestling with your monkey mind or tight hamstrings during meditation, then journal about that. If you felt strong in your warrior pose or open in your bridge pose, you can journal about that.

You can also journal about the specific action steps you will follow through on during the day that contribute to fulfilling your deepest intention. If you are in reflection mode, you can journal about how your actions did or did not contribute to your intention during the day.

Continue to journal for the entire five minutes, and if you can't think of anything to journal about, then you can address that!

This last part of the practice is important as all of the activities have prepared you for this written expression. I urge you not to skip it, especially for the first thirty days. Of course, as with all of the activities of the practice, if you have more to say, you can always journal longer.

# CHAPTER 11

# 30 BLOGS TO GRACE

In my own daily practice I turned some of my journaling expressions into blogs. I share them with you here to give you an idea of how resistance and surrender and everything in between can show up for you in a thirty day practice.

These were all written around my intention:
*I experience my life work with ease, rhythm, and flow.*

## Day 1

The first day I really fumble through, even though I am very familiar with the routine and thought I already had everything ready to go. I didn't have my favorite pen for journaling, and I forgot to wear a sweatshirt until I warmed up, so I was really cold. Even though I wrote it, actually practicing this *30 Days to Grace* is new to me, and it feels surprisingly awkward. I am tentative and excited about starting this new adventure, just to see what might be possible with this practice. I commit to doing it, every day, at least for the next thirty days.

## Day 2

Today was easier, at least the getting-out-of bed part was since my body still thinks it's an hour later with the Daylight Savings time change.

I felt more in touch with my breathing this morning but am still navigating my flow in the poses. I enjoyed the journaling piece the best today. Writing down my thoughts and feelings is really grounding and comforting to me. I didn't realize I had so many before I got I started!

I feel really good about myself for having two days of the practice under my belt, and it is feeling more possible and more accessible. I remain open. Open to the process and open to all the possibilities and opportunities available to me.

## Day 3

Big mistake today. I shut off my alarm and rolled over (for just a minute that turned into thirty minutes). Now I am late and rushing around to jump in the shower, figure out what I can wear, and drive to an early morning meeting across town. My dog threw up, my first choice for a blouse had a stain on it, and the traffic is heavier than I expected. My whole morning has turned into an "emergency."

But in spite of it all, I still did my practice. I feel more confident with the poses and can be in my body instead of in my head. With the different activities, I focus on my intention in different ways, through breathing, moving, meditating, and writing. Three days under my belt and the lessons keep coming. Tomorrow, I commit to not rolling over, not even for a minute!

## Day 4

Up today with the first faint beep of my alarm. It feels good to get out of bed immediately, brush my teeth, wash my face, and go directly to my sacred space. Lots of thoughts today, with my first *30 Days to Grace* program launching the CD tonight. How will it be received? Will they get it? Will they go home and do it? I really want to convey the possibilities this practice has to offer so they will be inspired to commit to it.

After my practice today, I feel relieved and not so overwhelmed, even though I have a thousand things to do in preparation for tonight. I am more grounded and calm, I open to a bigger vision, and I appreciate this event and all it has to offer. I vow to stay in the moment and in my heart and to enjoy the whole process: the errands, the setup, the anxiety, and finally the program. I open to grace.

## Day 5

Wow. I'm still reveling in last night's first public program of *30 Days to Grace*. There was a peaceful, open, and joyful energy in the room that was palpable. It was apparent to me that everyone in the room was open to grace.

Watching fifty people participate in my guided practice was a beautiful sight. And the many comments I heard afterward were even better!

*"This is exactly what I need in my life right now."*

*"I am reminded of how wonderful I feel when I take time for myself."*

*"What a simple, yet powerful program; I feel I can actually do it."*

The biggest testament to the evening was when the entire room committed to doing the practice for thirty days. I am eager to hear how everyone does and to support them on their journey in this life-changing practice.

## Day 6

Today it is hard to settle into my practice. I am ruminating about a conversation I had last night with a friend, and I am agonizing about a conference call I have today that I don't feel prepared for. Then, I start to notice how incredibly hungry I am and start thinking about what I can have for breakfast. And what about lunch? Then, I wonder what I might wear today, and I start playing a song in my head from an old movie. I am experiencing a severe case of monkey mind and my mind is wandering to and fro, wherever it wants to go!

I get glimpses of peace and calm, but mostly I wrestle with these thoughts again and again. Some days are like this, I am reminded. It's okay. I have shown up and met my monkey mind head on. I open to grace and remember I have tomorrow to practice again.

**Day 7**

Something has shifted in me. I don't feel like I am doing "the" practice but feel like I'm doing "my" practice. I have taken ownership and feel like it is my own. Even today, on Saturday, I got up without a second thought and went right to my sacred space.

I am also starting to notice I feel more calm, more present, and more conscious during my day. I pay more attention to my thoughts and actions. I even had a friend comment on how peaceful I seemed. I am observing these subtleties and am excited about the possibilities for the next twenty-three days.

**Day 8**

I love starting my day with this practice. It grounds me, centers me, and helps me set priorities. When I meditate on what the most important action is needed today to meet my intention, I realize I have a strong tendency to practice "approach fear."

Approach fear is the story we make up about how hard, or scary, or time-consuming something is going to be as we approach it, before we even get started. Of course, we make all of this up, and the fear we cultivate keeps us stuck, unable to move forward, which only leads to more fear.

The mantra that helps me with approach fear is, *"I always feel better when I take action."* In the middle of my biggest approach fear, I ask myself, *"What action can I take right now?"*

**Day 9**

Today I started my practice with gratitude. Gratitude for all the fabulous things going on in my life right here, right now: good health, loyal dog, beautiful home, close friendships, loving family, work that I have chosen and love, and all the possibilities that await me.

I choose gratitude because it keeps me in my loving heart instead of my fearful head. It keeps me focused on abundance instead of lack and limitation. It keeps me in celebration of all that is right, instead of bemoaning all that is wrong.

The glass is always half empty or half full. I just have to choose.

**Day 10**

Today I focus on release. I often find myself holding on to things tightly, not wanting to let go, of either an idea or a thought or feeling, even if it is not serving me. I can also hold on to relationships that no longer work—to projects or hobbies I am no longer excited about. I can even hold on to my anger or disappointment about someone or something, even though it keeps me resentful and irritable.

*What can I release today that no longer serves me?* When I release a feeling, person, or obligation that no longer serves me, I open to grace, open to something bigger, and set myself free.

Just for today,

*I release my judgment.*

*I release my partner to do what he needs to do.*

*I release my fear and worry of being alone.*

*I release my holding on to something that doesn't exist.*

*I release my need to know why and to understand.*

*I release my incessant wishing that things could be different.*

## Day 11

It was one week ago today that I initially launched my public program for *30 Days to Grace,* when everyone in the room committed to the practice for the next thirty days.

After checking in with the group, I am thrilled to know people are actually doing it and already feeling the positive effects! Now when I sit at my sacred space first thing in the morning, I can visualize fifty other people sitting in their sacred spaces. I do indeed feel like I am part of something bigger. Here are a few emails I received:

*"The practice is having a strong effect on me. It is giving me the impetus to make other small changes that build on my mindfulness and serenity as well."*

*"30 Days to Grace is providing me with exactly what I need: an easy practice, guided beautifully and gently, complete with journaling, which*

*allows for powerful reflection and an ability to track my progress."*

*"Wow! Thank you for reminding me how powerful this practice is. I am doing it daily again, and my whole life feels like it is back on track!"*

## Day 12

I woke up today on the wrong side of the bed. No particular reason—just felt grumpy immediately upon rising. I didn't want to do the practice today. I wanted to stay in bed and be mad at virtually everything and everyone. But I did the practice anyway.

I actually started laughing out loud in the middle of my deep breathing as I tried to rationalize my irritable mood. I couldn't really come up with anything very satisfying. And then I remembered my mood is a choice. My grumpiness is my choice. By the time I got to the yoga poses, I had forgotten how my day started and was totally into the flow. It was nice to get my grumpiness over with early in the day!

## Day 13

I ask myself today how engaged I am in my life. How engaged am I in my relationships, work, health, dreams, and anything else I participate in? Am I present, conscious, in the moment, or am I checked out, distracted, or asleep?

Today I observed myself in my practice and became acutely aware when my mind zoned out, slipping back into the past or speeding up into the future. It takes constant attention to be fully engaged: to focus on your breath, to move fluidly in the yoga pose, to train your busy mind to focus on your intention. How I show up for my practice is how I show up for my day.

I stay engaged today by asking myself, *"What do I need most to fulfill my intention today?"* And when my attention goes elsewhere, I bring myself back, again and again and again.

## Day 14

I was reminded yesterday how much everything can change in an instant. On my way to teach an early morning yoga class, I stopped at the end of my street and, thinking it was clear, proceeded through when I was sideswiped by an oncoming truck. My car spun around in slow motion for what felt like one hundred times and ended up in a neighbor's front yard.

Of course, it could have been much worse. No one was hurt. No significant property damage was done. The only casualty was my poor SUV that is probably totaled. After working for more than twenty years in the emergency room, I don't really believe in accidents, only warning signs.

Interesting that my focus was on full engagement yesterday, but apparently I still need some practice to pay attention, slow down, and be more conscious and awake. One way I can be more

engaged is to leave earlier for every appointment
and meeting so that my mind is not in the "hurry
up, gotta get 'er done" mode.

## Day 15

I am halfway through my thirty day practice, and
I woke up to 10 inches of velvety snow today. It
is absolutely beautiful, and, with no place I have
to go today, I am happy to stay home and create
a snow day. Yippee!

Snow days are really important in our lives.
Although we have no control over the weather,
we can schedule metaphorical "snow days" to give
us a chance to take a breath and exhale. I love a
snow day because it gives me permission to block
out an entire day without classes, appointments,
commitments, or errands.

Today for my snow day I am going to do exactly
what I want. I let go of my tendency to keep busy
and focus on my to-do list but engage in other
things I rarely make time for. Today, I will call
an old friend I haven't connected with in a while,
take a long hot bath without rushing, and read
the novel that's been on my nightstand for two
months. I love snow days!

## Day 16

I used to really dread Mondays. I would start
thinking about all I had to "get done" for the
week and become paralyzed. Now, I embrace the
first day of the work week by remembering every
Monday is an opportunity for a new beginning.

This daily practice has helped me embrace Mondays because I start my week like every other day, focused on my intention instead of my fear. I get to choose to focus on the weekend that is over, or I get to greet a new week knowing I can be in the flow with my work and with my life.

## Day 17

I did not practice this morning. I got up late, and I could have practiced after I taught my early morning yoga class or before my afternoon stress management class, but I did not. I wish I had a really juicy excuse, but I didn't.

I did practice this evening. I am glad I did it, but it doesn't have the same impact on me as my morning practice. The whole idea of starting your day with the practice is about setting up your day with intention, consciousness, and awareness. Practicing at the end of the day is more about reflecting on the events of the day.

I'm still glad I kept the promise to myself and completed my practice today. It gave me great contrast, and I know tomorrow I will get right back to it first thing in the morning so that I can enjoy the benefits all day.

## Day 18

This practice helps me to remember. I come to my sacred space, and I give myself this gift of remembrance by focusing on how I can stay in the flow of my work through the different activities. It occurs to me that this may be the only dedicated time I have in my busy day to do this. I also know that my awareness has been primed this morning and that there is a certain level of remembrance that stays with me all day long.

In the midst of parking tickets and heavy traffic and contracts that don't come through, I still remember my deepest intention because I focused on it this morning. I may forget in moments, but then I remember again.

## Day 19

*How much is enough? What is a balanced life? Is it different for every one of us?* What I know about myself is that my balance consists of many things. I have to move every day but not so much as to become exhausted or injured. I have to connect with my friends and family but not too much or I get distracted.

I listened to two women discuss what they liked in a yoga class, before my class started yesterday. Not too fast but not too slow. Not too much talking but enough feedback and correction. Not too intense but not too easy either. Ah, in search of the perfect balance.

The same is true off of our yoga mats. We ride the pulsation of the ups and downs, the light and dark, the highs and lows. Life is never in total or perfect balance but instead in constant motion and change. I stay in the flow.

**Day 20**

I gave my program, *30 Days to Grace,* to a group of women at a Work Life Balance Conference yesterday, where I led them in deep breathing, yoga poses, meditation, and journaling. Afterward, one woman said she didn't like the yoga because it made her feel awkward and ungraceful. That, of course, is why I call this a practice. We show up and do our best, knowing that grace takes time.

We wouldn't expect to play classical piano without a lot of practice, so why should we expect to look beautiful practicing yoga the first few times? Someone once told me it is good to do things you aren't particularly good at or that aren't particularly easy. Yoga has always been very challenging for me, and I am still at it because I know it helps me open to grace. Some days it takes longer than others.

**Day 21**

They say it takes twenty-one days to make a habit. I think it probably takes a little longer, but twenty-one days is a great start. I know now that when I don't practice first thing in the morning, I feel like something is missing in my day. I somehow don't feel complete.

This is the beginning of establishing a habit, when you feel like something is missing if you don't do it. How wonderful it is to get used to something that makes you feel good, keeps you centered and intentional, and improves the quality of your whole day. I am happy with my new habit.

## Day 22

I am overwhelmed today. Everything feels impossible. Why do I have so many different things on my plate? Why can't I just be content with doing one thing really well? The whole ten thousand hours of practice haunts me. I know it is not in my true nature to do one thing really well. I often wish it was. It seems like life could be so much simpler if I just had one thing to do over and over again. And, I would be bored and underwhelmed, which would be worse. I embrace all of my opportunities and remind myself that being overwhelmed is a choice. I stay in the flow of my work and my life.

## Day 23

Today I step into the flow. I open to grace by trusting, allowing, and inviting all the good into my life. Everything falls easily into place as I receive great news about my car repair, reach a prospect on the first attempt, and am highly complimented by a client request.

Not all days can be this full of grace (like yesterday), but I can celebrate when they are. Of course, if every day was this blissful, one would not appreciate it. But today I absolutely revel in it. I claim my good, and I remember to remember all of this the next time I am riding the current and it is less favorable.

**Day 24**

I love this quote by Denis Waitley:
*"Happiness cannot be traveled to,*
*owned, earned, worn or consumed.*
*Happiness is the spiritual experience of*
*living every minute with love,*
*grace and gratitude."*

The daily practice helps me recall how to fall in love again, open to grace, and to practice gratitude by staying focused on my deepest intention. The activities support me to have a spiritual experience with myself and keep me present and happy. I am truly grateful to have this experience.

**Day 25**

I am feeling very small and fearful today. I would like to go to sleep in this moment and wake up tomorrow to start over again. And then my heart would not be broken wide open, my bank account would be full, and I would be happier and healthier and braver.

But today, in the midst of my fear, I know I am not alone. I am supported by the Divine and my friends and family and this practice. I practiced today, even though I fought it the whole time. I know tomorrow will be better. It always is.

**Day 26**

Yesterday, I skipped. I didn't skip the practice, but I skipped writing about it. My day was full, and I just never quite got around to doing it...

It was kind of scary to skip a day of blogging because I have been on such a roll. I didn't want to give it up altogether, especially when I am so close to nearing the thirty day mark.

So, today, as we celebrate Thanksgiving, I am putting off my turkey and dressing a little longer because I want yesterday to be only one day of skipping writing and not two or three or even ten. Just like the practice, I have created a daily habit, and the only way I can reinforce it is to practice it daily. So, today, I reflect on the habits I choose to create in my life with great gratitude.

## Day 27

Well, I had every intention of being mindful, present, and determined to make good choices yesterday at our Thanksgiving feast. I planned on eating a good meal but not overeating. Turns out, I still ate too much and did not feel great when I woke up this a.m. as I still felt full.

So, the first big celebration when the holidays get into full swing, and I did not do so well. I remember, again. I remember why I eat well and exercise often and do my practice daily. Because it makes me feel good, and I really like to feel good. Today I remember what is too much and what is not enough to keep my life full of love and grace and in the flow.

## Day 28

I had coffee with a friend who has been practicing *30 Days to Grace* for the last twenty-four days.

Her intention was *"Money is flowing into my life with fun and joy."* She says there have been many small miracles since she started to focus on her intention, but you have to be awake to see them.

A doorman at a hotel fixed the squeaky wheel on her luggage without even being asked. Another hotel gave her free Internet access. While she was taking her teenagers out for their birthdays and telling them about the power their thoughts have over their lives, a woman came to the table and gave them a coupon for two free desserts. *"Wow. This stuff really works!"* said her fifteen-year-old in pure amazement.

You have to look for the miracle, the synchronicity, the synergy or you might miss it. That is the whole idea behind the practice, to focus on your intention and then notice what happens because of your focus.

## Day 29

Today I focus on letting go. I let go of my un-realistic expectations of others. I let go of how I want things to be and see things for what they are. I let go of the need to be in charge of everything and everyone.

I embrace what Joseph Campbell says,
*"We must be willing to let go of the
life we have planned, so as to accept the life
that is waiting for us."*

Believe that there is more waiting for you, when you let go of what you are struggling so hard to hold on to. Letting go is not only the end of one thing—more importantly, it is the beginning of something else.

## Day 30

Wow! I made my thirty days to grace! I made my practice every single day, and I blogged about it every single day (okay, I missed one day). It feels great to have completed the thirty day practice but even better to have kept the promise I made to myself.

I have enjoyed the practice and writing about it. My life has shifted in the last thirty days because I have shifted in my alignment to be in the flow. I am excited to begin my next thirty days with a new intention. But today, I celebrate. I celebrate my commitment, my focus, and myself as I choose to experience my life work with ease, rhythm, and flow.

## CHAPTER 12

# OVERCOME YOUR RESISTANCE

*"If you have ever brought home a treadmill and
let it gather dust, quit a diet, a course in yoga
or meditation practice, if you are a writer who
doesn't write, a painter who doesn't paint, or
an entrepreneur who never starts a venture,
then you know what resistance is."*

— Steven Pressfield, author of
*The War of Art*

Resistance is my favorite topic to discuss, but I dread
actually experiencing it. I dedicated this last chapter to
it because we all encounter resistance on a daily basis,
and the only way to work through it is to, well, work
though it.

Any discipline you want to cultivate in your life, whether
it's eating more healthfully, calling your mother more
often, getting (and staying) organized, or engaging in a
daily practice, will bring with it resistance.

What exactly is resistance? It is the struggle and strife
we feel when we don't want to do something. It rears
its ugly head in a myriad of ways, from avoidance to
addiction, including:

Procrastination          Apathy

Minimizing               Depression

| | |
|---|---|
| Blame | Overdoing |
| Anger | Addiction |
| Frustration | Perfectionism |
| Paralysis | Rationalization |
| Distraction | Narcissism |
| Illness | Low Energy |
| Drama | Self-Sabotage |
| Avoidance | Overwhelm |

The biggest way resistance conveniently shows up is in some version of *"I don't have time for this!"* When I worked in the emergency room, many of my patients made this statement, whether they were dealing with a broken ankle or a heart attack.

It was a Monday morning when a forty-four-year-old impeccably dressed female rushed through the ER doors demanding pain pills. *"I'm having some jaw pain. I tried Ibuprofen, but I'm needing something a little stronger. And I'm in a hurry!"* she ranted breathlessly.

After I told her we would have to do a complete assessment before we could give her anything, she replied, *"Assessment! How long is that gonna take? I don't have time for this! I have to get back to work, take my boys to practice, and my mother-in-law to the doctor!"*

I noticed tiny beads of sweat forming on her forehead, and her face was ashen gray. After a little more questioning, it turned out Jill really hadn't felt well for two weeks. She was always tired and breathless after even routine activities, such as taking a shower or climbing the stairs. The whole time we talked, Jill was checking her watch, staring at her cell phone, and asking me, *"Are we about done?"*

After a few tests, it didn't take long to recognize Jill was having a heart attack. She was scheduled for a cardiac catheterization that afternoon, but when I went into her room to tell her, she was gone!

Jill had left the building because she didn't have time for a heart attack. She was "too busy" taking care of her two bosses, her three boys, and her sick mother-in-law.

How ridiculous is it to think you don't have time for your own heart attack? What could possibly be more pressing? Since my *30 Days to Grace* practice is not an emergency, and most likely a huge departure from what you normally do for the first thirty minutes of your waking hours, it can easily be dismissed in favor of something "more important."

When I give my programs, in an all-day workshop or an opening keynote, the audience members always feel positive and upbeat after they experience the practice. They create their intentions, sign their contracts, and commit wholeheartedly to practicing for thirty days.

Then, a few days later I start getting emails about special projects, sick kids, unplanned trips, overwhelming remodel jobs, and all sorts of things going on in people's lives. They plan to get to it after X, Y, or Z. For these people, so full of hope and promise initially at my program, resistance has won.

It's quite convenient to blame outside sources that keep us too busy to start or continue something that requires us to do our own internal work. Resistance helps us avoid acknowledging what we really want, who we really are, and what is most important.

I like to think of resistance as driving with the brakes on. Even if we know what is most important, we hesitate, procrastinate, and drag our feet by driving with the brakes on. Why?

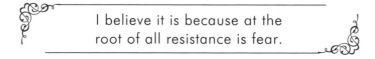

I believe it is because at the root of all resistance is fear.

We are not just afraid; in fact, we are terrified. We are terrified of losing ourselves and terrified of finding ourselves. Terrified of failure and terrified of success. We somehow feel safe and comfortable, even in all the discomfort of our less-than-satisfying lives. Resistance plays right into this false sense of comfort.

I witnessed high resistance every day in my coaching work at an intensive outpatient mental health program. Our clients functioned at all different levels and entered our program in a great deal of pain due to mental illness, ranging from depression to post-traumatic stress syndrome to addiction. Even though dire circumstances, such as bankruptcy, divorce, chronic illness, and jail time often plagued them, they were still resistant to changing their behaviors because they had become so familiar and comfortable with their pain and suffering.

We taught our clients new life skills to deal with their mental health and the resistance they had in dealing with their mental health. Like everyone else, they also had to deal with everyday life issues, and a daily practice provided a structure to help them focus on what was most important.

This daily practice requires you to create and maintain a new habit. A habit consists of four parts, all equally important:

Habit = Knowledge + Skill + Desire + Practice
(what)        (how)      (want)       (do)

The knowledge of *what* to do is outlined in this book. The CD guides you through the daily practice to learn *how* to do the different activities. The desire comes from within you because you *want* to do something different. The actual *doing* comes from you as well, when you honor your commitment to practice every day.

To develop this new habit, you must be prepared to deal with resistance. Here are the steps to follow that can help you overcome it:

1. **Acknowledge**
   Acknowledge when your resistance comes up, in the form of excuses, rationalization, and *"yeah, but"*...without giving energy to analyze it. It isn't

so important to know why you aren't doing it, as focusing on the reasons can be just another distraction.

Acknowledge that you aren't doing it and then choose to do it. In other words, don't think; just do.

2. **Visualize**

   Keep your intention in sight so you have a visual reminder of what is most important to you. Mark off the days you practice on your calendar so you can take credit for your commitment. Create a vision board with your intention statement and meaningful pictures and images. Place a touchstone someplace you can see it every day to remember what matters most.

3. **Prepare**

   Set yourself up for success by scheduling this practice every day, just like all the other appointments you make. Announce to your family members your new routine so they are not taken off guard. Lay all your yoga clothes out the night before. Be disciplined about getting to bed earlier so you can get up earlier.

   Before you go to bed, make the decision about when to get up, instead of waiting until the dark, cold morning when your alarm goes off. If you wait, the warm and comfortable bed will likely win.

4. **Stay Present**

   Many of us experience resistance most when we are feeling overwhelmed and think of all the things we have to do, instead of focusing on what's right here, right now. Be in the moment.

This practice will help relieve your stress, worry, and feelings of being overwhelmed. You will have more time in your day because you will have more presence and focus.

5. **Remember**
*"I always feel better when I take action."*

You have to remember why your deepest intention is so important, every day. Practicing every day reinforces how important your intention is, and remembering how important your intention is provides reinforcement for you to practice every day.

Implement the three day rule. Never let resistance win for more than three days. I know from all of my coaching experience that one day becomes two, two become three, and then all of a sudden you realize you haven't practiced for a month!

6. **Commit Again**
Repeat steps one to four again as necessary. As Fred from *The Wonder Years* sitcom said, *"Change is never easy; you fight to hold on, and you fight to let go."*

The persistence to commit again and again and again is the only way to overcome your resistance. When you are willing to stay the course, even when it's uncomfortable, inconvenient, and unorthodox, you will break through your old behaviors, patterns, and habits that are not working. When you overcome your resistance, you will remember how powerful, creative, and deserving you really are.

All you have to do is open to grace and show up for yourself.

And now you know how.

# BIBLIOGRAPHY

Addington, Jack and Cornelia Addington. *The Joy of Meditation.* United States: DeVorss & Company, 2005.

Cameron, Julia. *The Artist's Way: A Spiritual Path to Higher Creativity.* New York: Penguin, 2002.

Cameron, Julia. *The Right to Write: An Invitation and Initiation into the Writing Life.* New York: Penguin, 1998.

Dreamer, Oriah Mountain. *The Invitation.* New York: HarperCollins, 1999.

Gladwell, Malcom. *Outliers: The Story of Success.* New York: Hatchette Books Group, 2008.

Hanson, Judith. *Living Your Yoga: Finding the Spiritual in Everyday Life.* Berkeley: Rodmell Press, 2000.

Hanson, Judith. *30 Essential Yoga Poses for Students and Their Teachers.* Berkeley: Rodmell Press, 2003.

Hanson, Judith. *Relax and Renew: Restful Yoga for Stressful Times.* Berkeley: Rodmell Press, 2011.

Iyengar, B.K.S. *Light on Yoga.* New York: Schocken Books, 1976.

Kabat-Zin, Jon. *Wherever You Go, There You Are: Mindfulness Meditation in Every Day Life.* New York: Hyperion, 1994.

Kempton, Sally. *Meditation for the Love of It: Enjoying Your Own Deepest Experience.* Boulder: Sounds True, 2011.

Kirk, Martin and Brooke Boon. *Hatha Yoga Illustrated: For Greater Strength, Flexibility, and Focus.* United States: Human Kinetics, 2006.

Lewis, Dennis. *Free Your Breath, Free Your Life: How Conscious Breathing Can Relieve Stress, Increase Vitality, and Help You Live More Fully.* Boston: Shambhala, 2004.

Lewis, Dennis. *The Tao of Natural Breathing: For Health, Well-being, and Inner Growth.* Berkley: Rodmell Press, 2006.

Lipton, Bruce. *Spontaneous Evolution: Our Positive Future (and a Way to Get There from Here).* India: Hay House, 2009.

Lipton, Bruce. *The Biology of Belief: Unleashing the Power of Consciousness, Matters, and Miracles.* India: Hay House, 2008.

Maurine, Camille and Lorin Roche. *Meditation 24/7: Practices to Enlighten Every Moment of the Day.* Kansas City: McMeel Publishing, 2004.

Pressfield, Steven. *Do the Work! Overcome Resistance and Get Out of Your Own Way.* United States: Do You Zoom, 2002.

Pressfield, Steven. *The War of Art: Break Through the Blocks and Win Your Inner Creative Battles.* New York: Warner, 2002.

Sparrowe, Linda. *The Woman's Book for Yoga and Health: A Lifelong Guide to Wellness.* Boston: Shambhala, 2002.

Weil, Andrew. *Eight Weeks to Optimum Health: A Proven Program for Taking Full Advantage of Your Body's Natural Healing.* United States: Random House, 2006.

# ABOUT THE AUTHOR

## DIANE SIEG, RN, CYT, CSP

With a career that has taken her from the chaos of the emergency room to the calm of her yoga mat, Diane discovered yoga as a great source of healing during a personal crisis and has been practicing ever since. Diane worked as an emergency room nurse for over twenty years in hospitals across the country and her first book, *Stop Living Life Like an Emergency: Rescue Strategies for the Overworked and Overwhelmed* (LifeLine Press 2002) has helped thousands get out and stay out of the emergency room of life. Today, as a professional speaker, published author, life coach, and yoga teacher, Diane empowers people to live their most intentional lives, both on and off the mat through her keynotes, seminars, international retreats, coaching sessions, and yoga classes. She holds the Certified Speaking Professional (CSP) designation, the highest certification for a speaking professional, earned by less than 10 percent of the professional speakers in the world.

Diane lives in Denver, Colorado, with her life partner, Neil, and their beloved golden retriever, Buck.

*I would love to hear from you about
your experience with 30 Days to Grace!*

www.dianesieg.com
diane@dianesieg.com
www.30daystograce.com
888-586-8092

## Other works by Diane Sieg

*Stop Living Life Like an Emergency!
Rescue Strategies for the
Overworked and Overwhelmed*

*30 Days to Grace CD; A Daily Practice to Achieve
Your Ultimate Goals*

This CD leads you through the daily practice with
guided instruction on each activity and calming music.

# GIVE THE GIFT OF *30 DAYS TO GRACE* TO YOUR FAMILY, FRIENDS, AND COLLEAGUES.

quantity

**30 Days to Grace**
The Practice Guide to Achieve
Your Ultimate Goals                    $19.95  x _____  =  _____

**30 Days to Grace CD**
A Daily Practice to Achieve
Your Ultimate Goals                    $19.95  x _____  =  _____

**STOP Living Life
Like an Emergency!**
Rescue Strategies for the
Overworked and Overwhelmed             $19.95  x _____  =  _____

**Shipping:**
Please add $6.45 for first product and
$3.00 for each additional item.              +    _____

                              **Total: $ _____**

Name _____

Address _____

Phone _____

Email _____

Credit Card # _____

Expiration Date _____  Security Code _____

Please make your check payable to Diane Sieg and remit to:
Diane Sieg, 2381 Clermont Street, Denver, CO 80207

Credit cards orders will also be taken by calling 1-888-586-8092.

Products also available online at
30daystograce.com, dianesieg.com, and amazon.com

For local bookstore ISBN:  978-0-9848327-0-5
Library of Congress Control Number:  2011962697